PUBLISHER: I
EDITOR: Sar
FRONT CO\
CONTRIBUT
Fadhil al-A:
Bassam Fra
William M
Anton Shammas, Paul Starkey, Mona Zaki

imon

CONSULTING EDITORS
Etel Adnan, Roger Allen, Mohammed Bennis,
Isabella Camera d'Afflitto, Humphrey Davies, Hartmut
Fähndrich, Gamal al-Ghitani, Erdmute Heller, Herbert Mason,
Hassan Najmi, Saif al-Rahbi, Naomi Shihab Nye, Yasir Suleiman,
Susannah Tarbush, Stephen Watts

EDITORIAL ASSISTANTS:
Charis Bredin, Maureen O'Rourke, Nisreen Ghandourah,
André Naffis-Sahely

PUBLISHING ASSISTANT: Agnes Reeve

LAYOUT: Banipal Publishing

CONTACTS:
TEL: +44 (0)20 7832 1350
WEBSITE: www.banipal.co.uk
EDITOR: editor@banipal.co.uk
PUBLISHER: margaret@banipal.co.uk
INQUIRIES: info@banipal.co.uk
SUBSCRIPTIONS: subscribe@banipal.co.uk
ADDRESS: 1 Gough Square, London EC4A 3DE
PRINTED BY Short Run Press Ltd
Bittern Road, Sowton Ind. Est. EXETER EX2 7LW
Photographs not accredited have been donated, photographers
unknown.

BANIPAL, ISSN 1461-5363, is published three times a year by
Banipal Publishing, 1 Gough Square, London EC4A 3DE

Fiction in Kuwait is supported by
al-Multaqa al-Thaqafi in Kuwait
(The Cultural Circle)

BANIPAL
Magazine of Modern Arab Literature

www.banipal.co.uk

Ismail Fahd Ismail

Bothayna al-Essa

BANIPAL 47
Magazine of Modern Arab Literature

Fiction from Kuwait

Mersel al-Ajami
Fatima Yousif al-Ali
Taleb Alrefai
Thuraya al-Baqsami
Basima al-Enezi
Bothayna al-Essa
Ali Hussain al-Felkawi
Hameady Hamood
Ismail Fahd Ismail
Yousef Khalifa
Suleiman al-Khalifi
Laila al-Othman
Waleed al-Rajeeb
Fawziya Shuwaish al-Salem
Saud al-Sanousi
Mona al-Shammari
Sulaiman al-Shatti
Hooda Shawa

Taleb Alrefai

Ali Hussain al-Felkawi

Mona al-Shammari

Laila al-Othman

BOOK REVIEWS

Saud al-Sanousi

BOOKS IN BRIEF

EVENTS

Sarah al-Hamad

Sonallah Ibrahim

For all information about the
2013 Saif Ghobash Banipal
Translation Prize and the Banipal
Trust for Arab Literature, go to:

www.banipaltrust.org.uk

Rabee Jaber

EDITORIAL

This issue of Banipal has required an enormous amount of time and effort, more, in fact, than any previous issue. The feature is much longer than those of all our previous issues. We were forced to postpone to the next issue several texts by Egyptian, Moroccan and Lebanese authors, and have also had to suspend the regular Guest Writer section so

as to allow space for the greatest possible number of Kuwaiti writers, having realised that excerpts from four or five novels alone were already taking up more than half the pages. The nature of the novels demanded these extra pages, so that each excerpt could appear as an organic whole, offering the reader a better insight into the full work.

In the early years of Banipal, perhaps around 2001, we began debating the idea of producing a feature dedicated to Kuwaiti literature.

After some deliberation, we decided to save the idea for later. On the one hand, Kuwaiti literary production still appeared to be dominated by a preoccupation with the effects of the Iraqi invasion of Kuwait and the country's subsequent liberation. Overall, they represented a direct reaction to the crime committed by the Arab neighbour. On the other hand, we did not perceive any new "faces" emerging on the literary scene, and had already published a number of Kuwaiti authors individually, including Laila al-Othman, Taleb Alrefai, Fatima Yousif al-Ali, Saadiah Muffareh and Ibrahim al-Khalidy.

From 2005 to the present day, however, it is fair to say that many new literary talents have emerged, particularly in the novel and short story genres that currently dominate Kuwaiti literary output, advanced by such figures as Bothayna al-Essa, Saud al-Sanousi, Ali Hussain al-Felkawi, Basima al-Enezi, Hameady Hamood, Mona al-Shammari and Yousef Khalifa,

During the meeting of Samuel Shimon with Cultural Circle members in Kuwait on 16 December 2012, he spoke about Banipal's experience of translating and promoting Arabic literature in English, and answered many questions, most of which concerned how the west looks at modern Arabic literature, and the criteria western publishers consider in choosing an Arabic novel for translation and publication.

whose works form the core of our current issue. There are yet more names, which the pages of this issue are unfortunately unable to accommodate. These include Mais al-Othman, Istabraq Ahmad, Sa'da al-Da'as and Abdel Wahab al-Hammadi. We will most certainly return to their work in future issues.

So, how did the idea of producing this issue arise?

In the summer of 2012, the idea of publishing an issue on Kuwaiti literature was raised once again, this time by celebrated Kuwaiti author Taleb Alrefai. We exchanged many emails and talked at length on Skype. Last November, we happened to meet in New York and every morning for three days we sat in the Barnes & Noble bookshop café in Union Square before sauntering through the streets, all the while discussing the trials, tribulations and triumphs of Arabic literature and focussing – of course – on Kuwaiti literature. Taleb told me about al-Multaqa al-Thaqafi (the Cultural Circle) that he and his Kuwaiti friends, both writers and non-writers, had founded. He suggested that Banipal and the Cultural Circle should work together to produce an issue on fiction in Kuwait. I remember telling him that, for Banipal to produce such an issue, I would have to visit the country, in order to experience its literary scene directly and meet with its authors.

In December 2012, the Cultural Circle invited me to Kuwait. During my week there, I was delighted to meet a great number of Kuwaiti authors and to attend various literary events organised by the Writers' Association as well as the regular Tuesday Gathering (Multaqa al-Thalatha'). I also visited bookshops, museums and literary establishments, returning to London laden with new books and friendships.

To return to the beginning of this editorial, I must reiterate the great amount of time and effort we have spent producing this issue, which includes making selections from the novels and short stories of the 17 Kuwaiti authors in the feature, whose collective work spans the generations, beginning with the 1960s and the writing of Sulaiman al-Shatti, Ismail Fahd Ismail and Suleiman al-Khalifi, then moving on to that of Fatima Yousif al-Ali, Laila al-Othman, Waleed al-Rajeeb, Taleb Alrefai and Fawziya Shuwaish al-Salem and finishing with works of the young authors Bothayna al-Essa, Saud al-Sanousi, Basima al-Enezi, Ali Hussain al-Felkawi, Hameady Hamood and Mona al-Shammari. It is a great pleasure to present this wonderful selection of Kuwaiti literature to you and I hope you enjoy reading it.

I must also offer heartfelt thanks to my dear friend Taleb and to the members and friends of the Cultural Circle, who all contributed to producing this beautiful "book".

SAMUEL SHIMON

Follow us on twitter @BanipalMagazine
https://www.twitter.com/BanipalMagazine

Fiction from
Kuwait

Mersel al-Ajami, Bothayna al-Essa,
Ismail Fahd Ismail, Yousef Khalifa,
Laila al-Othman, Ali Hussain al-Felkawi,
Waleed al-Rajeeb, Mona al-Shammari,
Taleb Alrefai, Thuraya al-Baqsami,
Hooda Shawa, Hameady Hamood,
Fatima Yousif al-Ali, Sulaiman al-Shatti,
Fawziya Shuwaish al-Salem,
Basima al-Enezi, Suleiman al-Khalifi,
Saud al-Sanousi

*Al-Mubarakiya School, Kuwait's first state school, was established in 1911
and played an essential role in developing openness to modern science and
knowledge and revitalising Kuwaiti society.*   *Photo: Samuel Shimon*

MERSEL AL-AJAMI

A Brief History of the Short Story in Kuwait

THE PIONEER GENERATION

The short story emerged in Kuwait when objective conditions fostered a climate which could on the one hand accept this new literary genre, and on the other invest in its reforming potential. A number of pioneering factors contributed to providing the objective conditions: the spread of education, public libraries, literary salons and participation in pan-Arab magazines. Although these conditions may appear mundane to the reader in Kuwait at the dawn of the third millennium, by comparison with those living at the beginning of the twentieth century, they were of great and self-evident significance for the enlightenment of society and the dissemination of calls for reform.

The great historian Abdul-Aziz al-Rasheed presents, in his *History of Kuwait*, a lively picture of the great ideological conflict between those pioneers and some of their detractors who saw in this new opening-out a kind of blasphemy or heresy. Al-Rasheed distinguishes between two intellectual stages in Kuwait: the first running from Kuwait's foundation to the beginning of the twentieth century; the second in the first quarter of the twentieth century itself. While the first period witnessed some cultural activity and the emergence of a few poets, along with distinguished scholars like Abdullah Khalaf al-Dahyan, the general social environment was immersed in traditionalism and averse to any form of innovation. Suffice to say that the reading of Arab newspapers and magazines, education and

Mersel al-Ajami

schooling were only semi-systematic, while studying English was considered either apostasy or heresy by some men of religion. Abdul-Aziz al-Alji is one of the leading representatives of the trend that resisted any innovation or modernisation. Al-Alji's extremism was such that he would denounce anyone who read Egyptian magazines as an unbeliever, oppose any attempt to introduce modern schooling and viewed Muhammad Abduh and his pupil, Rasheed Ridha, as brazen heretics.

In the face of this intolerance, extremism and narrow-mindedness, a new generation emerged calling for openness to modern science and knowledge, for the advancement of society out of its ignorance and the control of despots. Abdul-Aziz al-Rasheed describes what occurred in the intellectual life in the first quarter of the twentieth century as an "astonishing upheaval", arguing that there were four reasons behind this revitalisation of Kuwaiti life:

1) The establishment of the quasi-state schools Al-Mubarakiya[1] (in 1911) and Al-Ahmadiya[2] (in 1921);

2) the emergence of an educated younger generation, which provided the basis for the foundation of literary associations for the first time, such as Al-Jama'iya al-Khairiya (The Benevolent Society) in 1913, Al-Maktaba Al-Ahliya (The Community Library) in 1922, and Al-Nadi Al-Adabi (The Literary Club) in 1924;

3) the launch of newspapers and magazines, particularly Egyptian ones, for it was via these that the Kuwaiti culturati could tap into what was happening in the Arab world, both in politics and literature;

4) visits by leading cultural and political figures to Kuwait, such as those by Abdul-Aziz al-Tha'alibi and Rasheed Ridha, which stoked intellectual debate within the country.

If Abdul-Aziz al-Alji was the voice of exclusion and intolerance, Abdul-Aziz al-Rasheed led the call for renewal and tolerance. De-

Fiction from Kuwait

Abdul-Aziz al-Rasheed

spite the optimism in al-Rasheed's "astonishing upheaval" phrase, the voice of intolerance and narrow-mindedness did not vacate the social scene, but remained prominent within the community. It was strong, too, in restricting the curriculum in al-Mubarakiya School, prompting its leaders to start again at al-Ahmadiya School, with its progressivist curriculum that included English language and modern science.

In order to refine its influence and effectiveness, this new generation adopted a viewpoint confronting the voice of reclusion and extremism. Abdul-Aziz al-Rasheed, supported by this pioneering milieu, realised the greatest achievement of the period: the inauguration of the *Majallat al-Kuwait* (Kuwait Magazine) in 1928 – the first magazine to be published in the Arabian Gulf. It seems there were two purposes of this magazine: the first was to create a channel through which the pioneering generation could advance its reformist agenda in all fields – social, religious and national; the second was to provide a way for Kuwaiti writers to disseminate their cultural and literary essays.

Al-Rasheed entirely succeeded in his aims, being able to publish a multitude of articles calling for reform, the combat of ignorance and backwardness and the rejection of isolationism and extremism. A great number of poems, literary discussions and translations of certain Kuwaiti and other Gulf writers also appeared in the magazine. The greatest surprise came when he published famous poet Khaled al-Faraj's first short story "Munira", the first Kuwaiti short story to appear in the magazine. Al-Faraj's involvement with and warm welcome of the magazine was a signal of his faith in the role the short story could play in the movement for reform, especially where it successfully expressed pioneering voices in the struggle against ignorance.

Thus the short story was born into the bosom of the publishing

Khaled al-Faraj

world. Khalid al-Faraj's short story "Munira" – the first in the Gulf, as well as Kuwait, was published in Parts 6 and 7 of the second volume of *Majallat al-Kuwait* (in November–December, 1929). The Munira of the story is a remarkably beautiful young girl living under constant scrutiny and supervision, who ends up a broken, suicidal woman. The tale's message is for external beauty to be combined with internal beauty by fighting ignorance with education and backwardness with enlightenment. The writer thus aspires for a future beyond the all-encompassing oppressive present. Thus enlightenment took its first steps with *Majallat al-Kuwait*'s publication of this short story, something which would bear much fruit for the future in the context of a then emergent form.

THE "SCHOLARSHIP" GENERATION

The final issue of *Majallat al-Kuwait* appeared in March 1930, and Kuwait's first foray into literary journalism was snuffed out. Six years later, Kuwait went through a severe economic crisis triggered by two causes: the inauguration of the pearl diving industry in Japan, which dealt a blow to the heart of Kuwait's pearl production; and the King Abdul-Aziz's embargo on Kuwaiti exports to Saudi Arabia, which struck at commercial trade. These factors bankrupted many traders, something which seriously reduced the sources of income for the two schools, Al-Mubarakiya and Al-Ahmadiya. They might have closed if not for the intervention of certain rich Kuwaiti businessmen, who asked the Emir to raise taxes from 4.5 to 5 per cent in order to fund educational development. When this proposal was acceded to, it also saw the established of the Majlis al-Ma'arif (Education Council) to oversee academic advancement. One year after its establishment, the number of schools had increased from two to ten, while the first girls' school opened in 1937

Fiction from **Kuwait**

in the face of opposition from some radical religionists. In 1939 the first student delegation – of only four – was sent to Egypt. It included Abdul-Aziz Hussain, who came to play an important role in education and culture in the years to come. The second delegation in 1943 consisted of 17 students, and the third – in 1945 – of 50. Given the increase in the number of students in Egypt and the provision of administrative supervision, it was decided to found the Bayt al-Kuwait (House of Kuwait) in Cairo to achieve two related goals: to pursue scholarship and to provide reassuring supervision on behalf of authorities and parents whose children were abroad.

In 1946, the House of Kuwait published the magazine *Al-Bi'tha* (The Scholarship), in which appeared what one might call the new voice of this "scholarship" generation. *Al-Bi'tha* is important for a number of reasons:

It provided for the voice of a new generation, thus contributing to the cultural and intellectual renaissance increasingly effectively over time. It suffices to allude only to Abdul-Aziz Hussain, Ahmad al-Udwani, Hamad al-Rajeeb and Abdullah Zakaria al-Ansari to establish the depth of the contribution made by this generation to modern Kuwaiti culture, in every sense of that word.

The magazine drew to it writers from the delegations, from Kuwait and from the Arab world more broadly. It opened Kuwait up to modern culture through ideas, fostering reforming and modernising agendas through treatises and debates on burning issues dividing the two distinct halves of Kuwait society.

It contributed to the dissemination of the short story form once again, publishing 64 stories incorporating the reforming voice of this new generation. Thus, Fadhil al-Khalaf focuses on the familial relationships in the Kuwaiti home and the persecution that women suffer in those situations, while Fahd al-Duwairi focuses on general social reform and Jassim al-Qattami concentrates on the oppressive conditions faced by seafarers in the social conditions prevailing at the time.

The magazine gave space to female voices from this generation. Thus the short story "Al-Intiqam al-Rahib" (The Terrible Revenge) deals with women's oppression in a patriarchal society with a moral courage and mature technique that would be inspiring to women writers of generations to come.

The magazine disappeared in 1954 at the height of its powers.

Al-Bi'tha magazine cover

The nascent media faced suppression and banning from 1959 for political reasons, returning only after independence in 1961. After this, most of the "scholarship" generation gave up writing, especially on social and educational matters. It seems to me that this was due both to intellectual reasons and new obligations. From the intellectual perspective, the generation obtained much of what they had called for. In terms of obligations, many of this generation took up ministerial and senior official positions in the newly independent state, thus being able to achieve in the real world what they had long called for in their writings. Thus this generation played a foundational role in the modern Kuwaiti renaissance.

THE SIXTIES GENERATION

This generation saw a number of radical political and social developments. Politically, there was independence in 1961, the founding of modern state institutions through dedicated ministries, elections to the Constituent Assembly and adoption of a constitution in 1962, and elections to the People's Assembly in 1963. Kuwait was moved from an emirate under British protection along the democratic path affirmed in the new constitution. Socially, the material boom which coincided with independence transformed Kuwait from a world of poverty to one of riches. Much of these riches were applied to health, education and social provision. The state became responsible for its citizens from cradle to grave.

These social and political developments needed a new generation to come to the fore that had lived through these changes and could therefore articulate Kuwait's dramatically new trajectory. Thus, after a decade, the short story returned, the reins held this time by new writers, the most notable of which were Sulaiman al-Shatti,

Suleiman al-Khalifi, Ismail Fahd Ismail and Abdul-Aziz al-Sari'a. This generation are regarded as having brought the short story form to the peak of its technical maturity, incorporating the best achievements of the Arab world on the one hand and establishing a basis for the launch of future generations of short story writers on the other, defining the grounds on which they could operate.

THE FOURTH GENERATION

By the fourth generation, I mean those who began publishing from the mid-1970s to the mid-1990s. Since this generation has been the subject of much study, I will make only brief allusion here to its contribution:

Women played a prominent role in this generation. Of the leading fifteen such writers, eight were women. This prominence of women meant that the position of the female in a male-dominated society came to the fore. Key figures in this regard are Fatima Yousif al-Ali, Alya Sha'ib, Laila al-Othman, Laila Mohammad Salih and Mona al-Shafa'i.

The preoccupations of men in this field varied between the fantasies of rejection and rebellion in Mohammad Mas'ud al-Ajami's work, the suffering of immigrants in that of Taleb Alrefai, images of violence and death in the work of Nasser al-Dhufiari, the duality of desert and city in Jassim al-Shammari's, and the preoccupations of the middle class in that of Waleed al-Rajeeb.

All that remains to be said is that, at the dawn of a third millennium, a new generation has begun to publish and those who have promise include Istabraq Ahmad, Mais al-Othman, May al-Sharrad, Basima al-Enezi, Mona al-Shammari and Sa'da al-Da'as.

Translated by John Peate

Notes:
1 Al-Mubarakiya School was established in 1911 and was Kuwait's first state school, named after Kuwaiti ruler Sheik Mubarak Al-Sabah.
2 Al-Ahmadiya School was the second state school to be established in Kuwait, inaugurated in 1921 and named after Sheikh Ahmad Al-Jaber Al-Sabah.

TALEB ALREFAI

An Overview of the Novel in Kuwait

Before oil, the social, intellectual and cultural ways of Kuwaiti life were simple, slow and ponderous, entirely interwoven with the hunt for food and shelter. It was a life beset by dangers, even existential ones, something which thus made cultural pursuits a luxury. After the discovery and export of oil, money arrived and all that accompanied it by way of the new and the modern. People consequently took up new ways, transformed the pattern of their lives, adopted new customs and habits, had dreams and visions previously unknown.

A noticeably new cultural scene advanced tentatively into an unwelcoming and conservative atmosphere, fostering a great deal of dialogue and debate, all of which conspired to shape the new artists and cultural activists of a modernised, advancing Kuwait.

Those who produce art reflect the realities around them, one way or another. Communal, cultural and intellectual life was enriched by this new-born, post-oil Kuwait. It inaugurated a new era in the nation's history and that spawned a diversity of literary innovations, including the novel.

The pioneering novels of the period 1948-1972 include Farhan Rashid al-Farhan's *Aalam Sadeeq* (The Sufferings of a Friend) 1948, Sabiha al-Mashari's *'Abath al-Aqdar* (The Futility of the Fates) 1960, Abdullah Khalaf's *Mudarrisa min al-Mirqab* (A Schoolmistress from Al-Mirqab) 1962, Ismail Fahd Ismail's *Kanat al-Sama' Zarqa'* (The Sky was Blue) 1970, Khalil Mohammad al-Wadi's *Ayh, Ayatuha al-Saghira* (Oh! little girl) 1970, Ismail Fahd Ismail's *Al-Mustanqa'at al-Dhaw'iya* (The Illuminated Marshes) 1971, Fatima Yousif al-Ali's *Wujuh fi al-Zuham* (Faces in the Crowd) 1971, Ismail Fahd Ismail's

Al-Habl (The Rope) 1972, Nuriya al-Sadani's *Al-Hirman* (Deprivation) 1972.

One can distinguish between the structure, plot and form of Ismail Fahd Ismail's works and those of others in that his works have their own particular forms and are preoccupied with broader Arab issues, making them significant not just at the Kuwaiti but also the regional level.

These were the ground-breaking Kuwaiti novels which articulated the preoccupations of their social environment. They did not fully incorporate the dimensions of the modern novel – something to be expected, given their embryonic character that was an expression of Kuwait's emerging modernity. In this regard, they took after emergent forms seen in all transforming societies.

The social issues associated with a new, emerging social atmosphere – with its new spirit, new customs, new dynamics – and in conflict with the tendency to yearn for the past, constituted basic themes for these first Kuwaiti novels, as did the world of womankind. It was as if these works narrated, in artistic form, the development of the new Kuwaiti society and its transformation from a simple, confined and conservative community into an expanding and dynamic one. These novels narrated the headlong rush into the embrace of the modern and the new, a world full of change and challenge – all the outcome of the discovery and export of oil. To access the new meant inescapably overhauling much of the nation's political, economic, social, intellectual and cultural structures.

Placing these novels in their historical context highlights the way in which they were a bold endeavour to mark out new paths for literature, and the Kuwaiti novel in particular. It is significant that the Kuwaiti novel began with the title of a woman's name and that three of the first eight had women's names in their title, clearly indicating that the female protagonist had come to the fore from its very beginnings.

Between 1973 and 1985, Ismail Fahd Ismail was the sole voice of the Kuwaiti novel to be heard in the broader Arab novel. In this period he wrote seven novels – from *Al-Dhifaf al-Ukhra* (The other Banks) in 1973 to *Al-Nil yajri Shamalun* (The Nile flows North) in 1984.

The year 1985 witnessed *Al-Mara'a wa al-Qitta* (The Woman and the Cat) by Laila al-Othman: an evocation of pre-oil Kuwaiti society,

Ismail Fahd Ismail

the secrets of an enclosed world, a world of the sea, a brutal dominion of oppression and suppression, a realm enclosing the marginalised and oppressed woman: the sister, the lover, the wife – familial oppression and male dominance from birth to death. Reinforcing her place in the Kuwaiti novel's history, al-Othman then produced *Wasmiya takhruju min al-Bahr* (Wasmiya comes out of the sea) in 1986. It was this novel which established al-Othman's particular voice and allusiveness. It drank from the same well that *Al-Mara'a wa al-Qitta* drew its water from, conjuring up Kuwait's 1950s, times before oil. These two novels and Waleed al-Rajeeb's 1989 work, *Badriya*, marked what one might call the second birth of the Kuwaiti novel, after which many more examples flowed.

THE KUWAITI NOVEL TODAY

The observer of the Kuwaiti literary scene will distinguish new voices emerging in the novel after 1989, with a distinctive tone and diversity of events and characters. They sketch out new contours for the Kuwaiti novel.

The most important names on the Kuwaiti scene today – alongside Ismail Fahd Ismail, Laila al-Othman and Waleed al-Rajeeb – are Taleb Alrefai, Fawziya Shuwaish al-Salem, Saud al-Sanousi, Hamad al-Hamad, Mais al-Othman, Suleiman al-Khalifi, Bothayna al-Essa, Haitham Budi, Sa'ada al-Da'as and Basima al-Enezi.

Any novel is, of course, a self-contained world, demanding deliberate and serious study in all its dimensions. We will therefore confine ourselves here to outlining the chief shared principles of the contemporary Kuwaiti novel:

There is an incorporation of social struggles, viewed highly objectively in the Kuwait novel, especially the twists and turns of relationships between men and women.

Fiction from Kuwait

Saud al-Sanousi

Bothayna al-Essa

Mais al-Othman

Abdel Wahab al-Hammadi

With the exception of Ismail Fahd Ismail's works, most novels can be said to be of the realist school – in their style, language and structure – to one degree or other.

The environments of the modern Kuwaiti novel, taken together, provide insights into the raging debates of contemporary Kuwaiti society. The narrative structure is one of the all-seeing storyteller, first person narrator or direct voice. Linguistic experimentalism is rare in these works, with the exception of those of Fawziya Shuwaish al-Salem, who deploys high poetic style open to experimentation.

There are evident autobiographical elements in the narratives, to one extent or another. Laila al-Othman's *Al-Muhakama* (The Trial) is quintessentially autobiographical. Similarly, Taleb Alrefai's *Dhill al-Shams* (Shadow of the sun) and *Samar Kalimat* (Samar's words) are inhabited by his own personal imaginations.

A significant proportion of the novelists are young: Abdul Aziz Mohammad Abdallah, Mais al-Othman, Bothayna al-Essa, Haitham Budi, Saud al-Sanousi, Basima al-Enezi, Abdel-Wahab al-Hammadi. They all represent a promising future for the Kuwaiti novel.

The National Council for Culture, Arts and Letters, Kuwait

The 1960s witnessed a great literary, cultural and artistic boom in Kuwait, encompassing numerous sectors of the society and reaching a pinnacle on 29 March 1972 as Prime Minister, Sheikh Jaber

al-Ahmad al-Jaber al-Sabah (later to become the Emir of the country), announced that a committee was to be formed, composed of the country's most important cultural and intellectual personalities. The purpose of this committee was to investigate methods of encouraging artistic and cultural revival in the country.

The committee was divided into four subsidiary groups, comprising Theatre and Cinema, Music and Folk Art, Plastic Arts, and General Culture.

Each sub-committee organised numerous meetings, conferences and discussions to assess the cultural and artistic situation in the country. On 29 November that same year, after six months of work, the committee submitted a detailed report to Sheikh Jaber al-Ahmad al-Sabah, recommending the establishment of The National Council for Culture, Arts and Letters (NCCAL).

On 17 July 1973, a royal decree was issued, confirming the establishment of the NCCAL, and thus consolidating the country's support for intellectual, cultural and artistic development. The second item in the decree specified the aims of the National Council as follows: "The Council will oversee all cultural, artistic and literary matters, working to facilitate growth and development in these areas and to enrich intellectual output. It will work to provide a

the National Council's headquarters in Kuwait City

suitable environment for literary and artistic production and to propagate culture through methods deemed appropriate. It will also focus on the conservation and scientific study of the country's cultural heritage. It will strive to increase interest in culture and the appreciation of Fine Arts and to strengthen ties with other Arab and non-Arab cultural bodies. It will instate a cultural programme, based upon objective studies of the needs of the country."

The Council's publications, which reach a wide Arab readership, can be considered essential elements of Kuwaiti culture today. They include the following:

the monthly magazine *Alam al-Maarifa* (World of Knowledge),
the periodical *Al-Thaqafa al-Alamiyya* (International Culture),
the periodical *Al-Ibda'at al-Alamiyya* (International Innovations),
the monthly newspaper *Al-Funun* (Arts).

Every year, the Council presents State Appreciation and Encouragement Awards to Kuwaitis who have excelled in different areas of creativity and culture. In addition, it organises a number of cultural and arts festivals, including Al-Qurain Cultural Festival, the Kuwait Book Fair, the Music Festival and the Festival of Children.

ADAM YOUSSOUF

Kuwait's Literary and Scientific Awards

Every year, a number of different prizes are awarded in Kuwait, both through governmental bodies and private organisations. Awards are dedicated to many different fields, including literature, thought and creativity. Perhaps the most famous of these prizes is the annual Kuwait State Appreciation and Encouragement Award. The winners of the award are announced shortly before the opening of Al-Qurain Cultural Festival and the results are eagerly anticipated by the entire scholarly community, for the prize holds great prestige and receives much media attention.

The Kuwait State Appreciation Award – a prize of ten thousand dinars – was launched in 2001 when Kuwait City was the Arab Capital of Culture. The Kuwait State Encouragement Award, meanwhile, was first awarded in 1989 in the fields of Arts, Letters and Social and Human Sciences, with prize money of five thousand dinars. Recently, however, the Council of Ministers announced that both awards would be substantially increased, with the Appreciation Award rising to twenty thousand dinars and the Encouragement Award to ten thousand dinars. This announcement met with widespread approval from authors and scholars alike.

Among other awards funded by governmental bodies is the annual Prize of the Kuwait Foundation for the Advancement of Sciences, which aims to support scientific research and encourage scholars and researchers in Kuwait and all other Arab countries. It is awarded in the fields of Basic Sciences, Applied Sciences, Economic and Social Sciences, Arts and Letters, and Arabic and Islamic Scientific Heritage. Every year, the Foundation assigns two awards of thirty thousand dinars to each of the above fields. The first is awarded to an individual or group from Kuwait and the second is awarded to an individual or group from other Arab countries.

Fiction from **Kuwait**

Author Laila al-Othman   *Sheikha Bassima Al-Sabah*   *Sheikha Suad Al-Sabah*

In addition to the above, there are several prizes sponsored by individuals or private cultural organisations. They include:

• The Foundation of Abdulaziz Saud Al-Babtain's Prize for Poetic Creativity, which is awarded every two years. The prize is composed of the Poetic Creativity Prize ($50,000), the Poetry Criticism Prize ($40,000), the Best Poetry Collection Prize ($20,000) and the Best Poem Prize ($10,000).

• The Suad Al-Sabah Publishing House Award, which is divided into four branches in the field of scientific innovation and four branches in the field of intellectual and literary creativity. It is awarded every two years.

• The Laila al-Othman Prize for Short Stories and Novels

• The Sheikha Bassima Al-Sabah Prize, devoted to members of the forum of new writers within the Kuwaiti Writers Association.

The Publishing Industry in Kuwait

The establishment of Al Mubarakiyya School in 1911 can be considered as heralding the arrival of modern systematic education in Kuwait. It was followed in 1913 by the Arab Charitable Association, which brought with it Kuwait's first public library. Meanwhile, *The History of Kuwait* (1928), by renowned scholar Abdul-Aziz al-Rasheed, is regarded as one of the most important historical reference works available to the people of Kuwait

Fiction from Kuwait

Suleiman Khalifi's novel *Biban*
published by *Dar al-Farasha*

Ismail Fahd Ismail's novel *Musk*
published by *Masa'a Publishing*

as well as throughout the Gulf and the rest of the Arab world. Farhan Rashed Al-Farhan's *Aalam Sadeeq* (The Sufferings of a Friend), published in 1950, was the first novel by a Kuwaiti author to be printed in Kuwait and after that presses began to flourish across the country. Amongst the most famous of Kuwaiti publishing houses are Al-Aujairy Bookstore, Al-Rabi'an Bookstore, Dar al-Arouba Bookstore, That al-Salasil Bookstore and Qurtas Publishing Co. In recent times, Kuwait has also seen the growth of publishing houses dedicated to literature by young Kuwaitis. The most prominent of these are Masa'a Publishing, founded by poet Mohammad al-Nabhan; Dar al-Farasha, founded by critic Fahd al-Handal and author Istabraq Ahmad; Dar al-Platinum (Platinum Press), founded by authors Ahmed al-Haidar and Jassim Ashkanani; Afaq Bookstore, founded by Dr Nasser al-Shammari; and Nova Plus for Publishing, founded by writers Khaled al-Nasrallah and Abd al-Wahab al-Sayyed.

These new publishing houses have met with great support and enthusiasm from young aspiring authors in Kuwait and acted as an incentive for them to enter the world of writing and publishing. The publishing houses are a vital factor in encouraging and fostering new talents and bringing debut works to the reading public. Their presence and their various activities have attracted great attention within the Kuwaiti literary scene, particularly amongst visitors to the Kuwait Book Fair where Platinum Press has launched 150 titles over the space of four years and Dar al-Farasha and Novo Plus for Publishing have each launched roughly 25 books every year.

Fiction from Kuwait

BOTHAYNA AL-ESSA

An Unexpected Encounter in Uppsala

EXCERPTS FROM A NOVEL
TRANSLATED BY CHARIS BREDIN

I cannot remember what happened that day. All I can recall is a sort of soundless collision. At the time, I was distracted, my mind was wandering absentmindedly over facts I needed to memorise, prayers my mother had taught me and the faces of friends, many miles away. I glanced around in search of my professor. After that, everything was a blur.

"Hey there!"

A voice ripped through my silence and a face loomed from nowhere, bearing a smile of hunger and rain. The prayers I had been muttering caught in my throat as I collided with a face that seemed to evade its own existence. I let out a startled yelp.

"*Bismillah!* In the name of God!"

"*Assalamu alaikum.* Peace be upon you."

You smiled in a strange, inscrutable way. I stumbled backwards, eying you cautiously and swallowing nervously.

Peace be also upon you, stranger that you are. Peace and blessings . . . deserts and talismans . . . home and exile. May my longing and my curses also be upon you.

Thus you descended upon me, a vagabond, and, with your so-called peace, you kindled a war within me. Were those really your words . . . *Assalamu alaikum?* You were a whispering from the devil, a paroxysm of incantations and chaos. May God grant me sanctuary from you! I gazed at you, unnerved by your incongruous presence in that foreign place. Your hair was smoothed with gel, scraped back

as though by strips of glue. Silver chains hung provocatively against your chest and a small tattoo of a scythe adorned your upper arm. Everything about you defied the words that came from your mouth and yet everything about you reminded me of a country I knew so well.

You burst suddenly and thunderously upon me, a lithe, tanned, Bedouin apparition that left me reeling. I stumbled back, gazing at you in horror and examining you unashamedly: regular Bedouin features and the bronzed, sun-kissed skin bestowed only upon you and your kind. Although mussed with gel, your hair was indistinguishable from that my brother's. On close inspection, even your fingers, with their long filed nails and silver rings, sent you back to the open desert, to milking camels and slaughtering beasts. Neither the chains, nor the rolled-up sleeves, nor the buttoned-down shirt, nor any of your other careful touches, could distract me from your long, sharp nose and the piercing intelligence that filled your eyes. Most conspicuous was your half-smile, a smile that has never reached completion on the face of any Bedouin throughout the ages.

You laughed at the marks of astonishment etched across my forehead. I floundered, lost in your features that were so stained with otherness. You repeated your greeting, your brown hand raised high.

"*Allah bil khair*, Yuba."[1]

Speaking in pure dialect, you resembled both everything and nothing as you stood there before me, a concentrated mix of home and exile. You seemed like a man split in half, divided in two by a rough red line, a modernist, multi-dimensional map stretching endlessly on . . . Who were you?!

"Kuwaiti?" I asked with difficulty, swallowing again.

Fiction from **Kuwait**

You pulled a strange half-smile, a smile that clearly testified to your churlish rejection of all identities and all things resembling an identity; a rejection that would have begun with your first gap-toothed smile and the first toy which you tore between your arms.

"Dhary," you replied in your own, resolute language, denying all concept of nation and belonging. You had no need to be anything but yourself. You alone were worthy of your belonging. You were a Bedouin myth, narrated not in the desert but under the shade of a pine tree, in a city of light and water. And so you came to me, the most elusive and intangible of beings.

You pointed to the badge on your chest where your name was written in foreign letters: D-a-r-i-e.

"Darie," I mispronounced.

Smiling, you shrugged your shoulders indifferently. "Call me Darie if you like."

Your rejection of everything, even your own name, was your first lesson to me. My cheeks blushed with embarrassment.

"Didn't Nizar Qabbani say that 'names are the most foolish thing we possess'?" you added with that same smile, your tone somewhat easing my consternation.

"I study biology. I don't read much poetry."

"But poetry is like the nation . . . it's for everyone."

Cold shame swept over me. Although I hailed from the heart of Najd, the soul of poetry, I was not armed with enough rhymes to confront the strangeness of our encounter. And what need had you of poetry when the world around you was filled with such beauty, when you formed part of such a rich green landscape?

You read the letters of my name on the badge pinned to my chest: "Fara . . . mouse!"

"No. Not Fara. It's Farah, joy."

You laughed. My eyes lit up with questions, but you cut in before I could utter a single word.

"The embassy told me you were coming."

"And who are you?"

"Dhary!"

You had no other form of identification, nothing but two eyes that shone with longing, defying the indifference you feigned as you thrust your hands into your pockets to conceal their excited trembling.

"They asked me to be your guide. But they didn't tell me you were a girl!"

"In that case, you're not obliged to continue."

"To be honest, this only makes it more exciting!"

I knotted my hands together, like two cats snuggling into one another. Your unexpected audacity had momentarily frozen my senses. It was as though you were unaware that honesty topped the list of all forbidden things!

4

You asked "How's Kuwait?", as though inquiring about a friend with whom you had lost touch. You may as well have asked: "Is she married? Or single and in love? Does she only receive unworthy suitors as always? Does she still hold her doors naïvely open for angels and demons alike? What's she up to, this saintly sinner? Does she abuse you and love you all in one go?

"Does she still push everyone away? Does she melt you down and fuse you together on a daily basis while you continue to love her more and more? Is she still full of contradictions and hypocrisies? Does she go nowhere and everywhere at the same time, advertising concerts while condemning musical instruments? Does she open her arms to all the world's hungry but her own? Do her shoulders sink beneath endless, hungry bites and glorified lovers who excel only at reeling off their poetry? Perhaps she has simply remained herself, captivating but impossible. How is she, my dear Kuwait?"

"Great!" I replied, stubbornly matching your dialect as an initial expression of national pride before we launched into our first long debate, retracing our steps along the path which snaked its way back to the halls of residence.

Around me, the streets of Sweden hummed with a beautiful, incomprehensible gabble. The strangeness of the place seeped coldly around me, descending from the trees and clouds, and rising from the snail shells and pebbles which scattered the streets. It emanated from every corner, from the smallest details of the city, gently numbing everything around me. It imbued you with an inexplicable melancholy.

"Is Al-Aujairy's bookstore still in front of the Nugra Shopping Centre?" you asked, your voice suspiciously curious.

"Sorry?"

"I remember that it used to be there . . ."

"It's still there."

"I also remember a palm tree . . ." you added after a long pause, "in the old Salmiya souk."

"A palm tree? What palm tree?"

"Never mind," you stammered, looking uncomfortable. A long period of tranquillity settled over us after that, stretching quietly and calmly on as though leading to the gates of heaven. Although swallowed in this listless silence, a strange sense of confusion rose within me. It felt wrong for us to be walking along the same street, chatting so casually.

"What would people say if they saw us together?" I wondered innocently.

"Why are you here on your own?"

"One of my friends was supposed to come with me but her family didn't let her."

You gave a wan smile whose meaning was quite clear: "Kuwait never changes!"

But then what about myself? Had I not spent a whole evening planting pleading kisses on my grandmother's forehead so that she would pressure my father into letting me go? How many times had I begged my mother to stop my brothers from scuppering my dreams? How much had I longed to participate in the Olympiad and proudly hold the Kuwaiti flag aloft? I stood before you, a lucky girl and no more!

"How old are you?" I asked.

"How old do you think I am?"

"Twenty-three."

"Twenty-six."

You were too old to be an undergraduate. I immediately guessed that you must be in Sweden for your Masters, but, following my train of thought, you quickly put me right.

"I've lived here for eleven years."

"Seriously?"

"Yes."

"That's weird."

You smiled without commenting.

"But why?" I mumbled, fearing to raise such a loaded subject.

"What a question!" you laughed, scratching the back of your head. "Isn't that an awfully long time?"

"Let's just say that, for me, Sweden beats Kuwait," you replied, clearly concealing other reasons behind this bland response. From that moment on, I could not dispel the impression that I was, in fact, in the company of a madman.

6

Peeping through a gap in the door, I followed the performance alongside the other inquisitive students. I was mesmerised by the Swedish country songs, my eyes fixed on the young girls flitting about the stage like petals falling from a pansy.

There were hordes of students outside the hall, awaiting their turn to enter and mount the stage to deliver their national anthems, enlivening the audience of academics who had flown in from all corners of the globe to give their blessings to the proceedings. The other delegations had at least three students each, and I was on the verge of collapse, not knowing how my lone voice could possibly do justice to little Kuwait. How could I communicate the soul of its sand, its blossoms and its seagulls, forcing my shaky voice into joyful ululations that would rise up to the heavens?

You were standing a few feet away from me, your arms folded. I could not but loathe you. Nothing concerned you, not the room, buzzing with national pride, not the sense of belonging among the other students, not the many, colourful flags . . .

"Why didn't the embassy find someone a bit more enthusiastic to be my guide?" I asked, not bothering to conceal my exasperation.

"Sorry to disappoint."

You were not prepared to convey any more emotion than that, or to tone down the blatant indifference with which you responded to everything that mattered so deeply to me. I turned away. You took a cigarette from your pocket.

"If this were Stockholm, it would be different. But Uppsala is out of the way. You'd be hard pressed to meet any Arabic speakers here."

"I was only wondering. How much are they paying you?"

You smiled, the cigarette pressed firmly between your lips.

"Not a penny."

"So why did you agree?"

"You're certainly not short on questions . . . but look out. You're on after the Koreans."

"Oh God!"

You smiled. Your hands were still buried in your pockets, signalling that you could not care less about anyone except yourself. My terrified eyes spoke volumes.

"Will you go on with me?"

"And sing on stage?"

"I'll pay you."

"Money costs dearer than national pride."

"I can't sing on my own."

"And what do you expect me to do about it?"

"Just stand next to me."

Your lips twisted into an enigmatic smile.

"Do you have a good voice?"

I cursed you inwardly, wondering why I bothered to put up with you.

The Iranian delegation entered the hall. My eyes fervently beseeched you, the terror in them more eloquent than words.

"I'm begging you!"

"Fine."

And then we were there, a pair of misfits, slouching awkwardly on the stage as we droned out our anthem with false emotion.

> *Kuwait, my country, may you be safe and glorious!*
> *May you always enjoy good fortune!*
> *Kuwait, my country*
> *Kuwait, my county*
> *Kuwait, my country, may you be safe and glorious!*

Shyness oozed from me in beads of sweat that shone on my glowing cheeks. I stole a glance at you. Pasty and incongruous, the only thing that united us was our coffee-coloured skin and our eyes, gazing absently into space. Our jarring resemblance was laid bare for the audience who sat before us, mesmerised by that strangest of spectacles, that most modern, most blasphemously burdensome of poetic images. Discomfort multiplied within me, endlessly reproducing like cells in the body. Tears welled in my eyes as I heard you churning our anthem out robotically, as though it stirred no emotion in you. The hall was empty except for you. You were concerned with no one. Nothing interested you, not even the words you were uttering. They meant nothing to you. You could have been singing simply for the pleasure of hearing your own voice, which happened to be rather pleasant. If I had asked you to perform the Nigerian or Norwegian anthem, you would not have hesitated. Shaking with nerves, I almost toppled over. I was on the point of clinging to you, cursing you and crying. What heinous crime had our country inflicted upon you that you treated it with such cold indifference?

We stepped down from the stage. I longed for the ground to swallow me up. You smiled to the audience.

"You have a good voice," you said, grinning.

7

Two days remained until the practical examination and one more until the theory. The supervisory committee had organised various outings to museums and churches so that the students could become better acquainted with Sweden's history. There was an awful lot to be said about a small city like Uppsala but you were not impressed, hiding your impatience behind a series of scathing jokes and acting as though the whole thing were a trial, inflicted from above. But it was me, and not you, who was being tormented by a companion caught in a swirl of cynical doubts, which he concealed beneath a shell of indifference.

A portly man was giving a lecture, standing some way off amongst the other students. We were grouped beneath a vast tree in the middle of a medicinal herb garden. The man was sporting a wig, adorned with white rolls of hair, and an old fashioned red outfit, composed of short breeches and light white stockings which made his legs look tiny beneath his protruding stomach. This was supposedly what Linnaeus had looked like, the world-renowned taxonomist and Uppsala's most famous citizen.

I felt ashamed to be attending a biology tournament when I did not even know who Linnaeus was. What had I been studying for the last two years? I could not hold back a wave of doubts, which I had been fighting off ever since my professor had maliciously insinuated that I might not be up to the examination. Everyone was listening intently to the lecture, nodding their heads as though the informa-

Fiction from Kuwait

tion was old news. I alone was lost in incomprehension. My face shone with perspiration. In vain, I tried to nod along with the rest.

"I have some bad news for you," the man began his speech. The students exchanged anxious, inquisitive glances.

"In 1778, I died," he continued in the same mournful tone.

Laughter rang out. The man's life-like rendition of the dead scientist's ghost immediately captivated me, but his speech soon exceeded my limited English.

"What's he saying?" I asked you excitedly.

"He's saying that he's the ghost of Karl Linnaeus, founder of taxonomy."

"I got that. What next?"

"Uppsala dedicated this special garden to him. Many of the plants in it are imported but they have become part of the city's heritage. Listen . . . this is pretty boring."

"Dhary!"

"Fine then . . . Linnaeus built this garden with his own hands in 1745 and lived his whole life here . . . Look at that old phoney pretending to be sad! He does the same thing every day, I swear! Anyway . . . can you see that small house at the end of the garden? That's his house. Linnaeus's, I mean, not the ghost's. It's been transformed into a museum. See what honour and glory do for you? The world ends up sanctifying your toothpicks and underwear. Did you travel all the way from Kuwait just for this?"

"You're leaving everything out . . ."

"Listen . . . it's stupid to pursue glory, particularly when you come from a part of the world trampled underfoot by Arabdom. Don't imagine for one second that you can become great in such a place without ending up as a pile of bones sooner or later. In English, the word 'great' is totally unconnected to the word 'bones' but in Arabic they're from the very same root. See what I mean? Will you care how great you were when you're stretched out underground with thousands of maggots?"

"Stop it!"

"Fine! Do you want to know how many times the Nobel Prize has gone to a Swedish man? Does that interest you, for God's sake? Do you want to know how many light years you are behind this crowd? They've won twenty-nine times. Do you want to know how many times the prize has gone to an Arab? Once . . . to Naguib Mahfouz!"

"And Ahmad Zewail?"

"He's not a proper Arab. He became Americanized."

. . .

Seeing me trembling in dismay, you gave a pitying smile and shook your head sorrowfully as though regretting your words and feeling pained at your own actions. With barely concealed bitterness and evident disingenuousness, you tried to repair the damage.

"Don't despair. It's obvious the prize doesn't add to any true genius. After all, it was only ever created to atone for the invention of dynamite. The jury simply selects a name on which to bestow fame so as to say to the world: 'Do you see? We are rewarding these great minds to make up for all the deaths we have caused. We are no longer culpable and will die with clear consciences. We bless you, your art, your science and your death! Nobel for peace!'"

"I don't understand a thing you're saying."

"All the better."

I was being corroded, I was shrinking before you. A desire to flee vibrated within me. I wanted to be anywhere so long as you weren't there. You had me penned in so completely, not only because of your superior knowledge nor because of the truth you were so eager to prove – that I came from the lowliest corner of the world – but because there was no concord between us. That was what made my sense of alienation multiply like a swarm of angry ants, burying into my pores as I silently howled in pain.

I could understand nothing that was being said. You must have noticed my bewilderment, for you began to interpret.

"In the Bronze Age, Uppsala was considered the most important city in Sweden because of its church and royal palace. It was also an active trade centre due to the Baltic Sea. And look over there . . . at that gigantic edifice built onto the Cathedral. That was where coronations took place. You can also see memorial statues dedicated to men who fought against the English."

"Were Sweden and England at war?"

"At a time when battles were more clear-cut. But listen . . . apparently, this monumental cathedral was built after the church burnt down in old Uppsala. The archbishop came here instead. Until recently bishops held a great deal of prestige and a fair amount of power, despite the fact that most Swedes consider Christianity to be more a social custom than a religion. Did you know that the state only split from the church a short time ago? In 1996. He also said that Archbishop Jacob Ulfsson founded the University of Uppsala in 1477. What were people in Kuwait doing at that time, Little Mouse?"

"There was no 'Kuwait' then. It's only existed since the middle of the eighteenth century."

"Excellent, Little Mouse, excellent. Listen . . . he's talking about the castle now. Perhaps I ought to take you there. You'd like it. Erik the Fourteenth lived there. He butchered a ton of people. So you see, even civilised countries were buried beneath skulls at one point. The Arabs are only just getting going! Apparently Erik was mad, though, and I'm not sure the same can be said for our lot. They're just scum, nothing more. Anyway, Erik's madness led to an armed rebellion in 1574. It failed, though, and he stayed on the throne for three more years before being poisoned by pea soup. Funny story, huh? Why can't we poison our dictators with peas?"

"Because peas don't grow in Kuwait."

"Good shot," you said, in impeccable English.

8

Life was certainly having a good laugh at me! You were my only window onto Kuwait, you who never missed an opportunity to aim another blow at the sanctity of my home. You threw one doubt after another at me, watching with evident satisfaction as my convictions came crashing down. That, in a nutshell, was our encounter: seven days that altered the course of my life, causing me to take up a pen and write of myself and of the burdensome sense of alienation, which still lingers even after all this time.

Life felt like an obscure, disorienting dream as I sat with you on the banks of a sparkling blue lake, clouds shimmering on its surface like houris bursting from Paradise. Yet there I was, cross-legged on a lush green carpet, in the company of a strange Bedouin. You had brought two cups and a pot of Arabic coffee with you, as though insisting upon reminding me of our precarious identity, the identity that you denied with loathing, even as it inhabited you with such passion.

I sipped the coffee slowly, floating through dark depths that awoke so many sensations within me: the scent of henna and oud oil and the vision of young girls dancing on TV to the songs of Sana al Kharaz and Shadi al-Khaleej. What memories it stirred in me! Coffee was the nation's best ambassador.

"It's delicious!" I congratulated you and your eyes lit up like a child's, your chest swelling with delight.

"Next time, I'll make Kuwaiti doughnuts for you," you added enthusiastically, "and anything else you want. I could make your trip so much more fun if you'd only stop squinting at those books like a madwoman."

"This is more important to me than it is . . . unimportant to you."

You peered in frustration at the biology textbook open on my lap. I was reading about phototropism as you ripped up tufts of grass in exasperation. You were in a talkative mood.

"Phototropism?" you interrupted me sarcastically.

"Yes. It means that plants bend towards the light."

"Do you also study emotional tropism?"

"Dhary!"

"I learned about it when I was little: plants like light and crawl towards it as though their life depended on it."

"Wrong! Auxins – which stimulate growth – are sensitive to light, causing them to move towards shadow, meaning that the shaded side of the plant grows faster than the sunny side."

"Aha! So that's what makes plants bend towards the light! Very plausible, but it doesn't convince me. If you want my opinion, any plant growing in Kuwait that considers bending towards the light is utterly crazed and needs a good dose of electric shock therapy. It'd get such bad sunstroke that it'd shrivel up and die. Have you ever heard of a feasibility study? It means you would consider it futile to read about plants leaning away from the shade in a place where there's no plants and no shade! Live a little, look at things as a poet and not a scientist. 'Poetry is the true antithesis of science.' That's what Coleridge said."

"Coleridge?"

"Yeah, he's my boss at work."

(Later, I learned that Coleridge was an English poet and that you had been mocking me mercilessly.)

Fiction from Kuwait

You smiled ironically. I gazed at you, feeling utterly lost, my sense of incomprehension increasing by the minute. You were enjoying all of it, prodding me as I groped around in a mist where nothing was certain and everything contingent, where, rather than bringing new truths, you simply plunged sharp, pointy doubts into my chest, watching at a distance as I pulled them in agony and patched up the deformities they left behind. Where were you heading with all this? You, who brought nothing but painful collision.

"Dhary?"

"At your service."

"What do you want?"

You released a long, deep sigh and a heavy weariness seemed to settle over you. This time, you tried to be gentler.

"Farah, my dear," you spoke softly, "Do you think I'm a bad man?"

"What do you want?" I repeated stubbornly.

You breathed deeply, as though trying to weigh up every word you spoke.

"Has it ever occurred to you that everything you do is a waste of time?" you asked, trying in vain to turn the tide of questions.

"What do you want?"

"What do you want? Tell me, why do you do all this studying, as though a hoard of demons were hot on your heels? For the sake of your country?"

"Of course."

"Excellent. Let's think about this a while. Why should I wear myself out living in one land rather than another and innocently calling it my country? Look around you, little one, and see how wonderful things are here. What examples do you need? The healthcare? The education? The fair distribution of wealth, which you can clearly see from the absence both of lavish palaces and toppling shanty towns? The only thing that Kuwait can brag about is having a lot of mosques and anyway didn't Mohammad say that 'the whole world has been made as a mosque for me'? True, winters here are long and depressing, but are we any happier with all our sunshine? Here, the world is at its most beautiful and I, Little Mouse, am in need of nothing. You are the one in need."

I eyed you suspiciously. Your smile betrayed your true feelings. I furtively observed your confusion as you lit another cigarette. You, like me, knew that what you had said was not enough. There had to be a more deep-seated and painful motivation for you to justify your departure so vehemently. It was impossible that you had based your choice simply on better healthcare and education. We had not yet reached that stage. The Arab spirit, so fond of instinct, follows its own logic when it comes to issues of belonging. Your reasoning may have appealed to the sort of Westerner who applies pure logic in all matters, but your Bedouin temperament, which is obvious even in the way you held your coffee cup, nullified all the fine rationale which you laid out before me. We understood one another. We knew that we needed reasons stronger than reason itself and logic to justify leaving our country. Reasons that were more emotional, more powerful and more present.

"That's the stupidest logic I've ever heard," I replied quietly.

"At least you're willing to call it logic."

"Are you a robot, Dhary? Do you not know the meaning of love?"

"For God's sake, let's distinguish between love and stupidity."

"No. Listen to me. You only ever listen to yourself. I mean love, love which allows you to love one thing above all else, not because it's more beautiful, but because you love it and that's what makes it beautiful. Kuwait is not as beautiful as Sweden, but for me it is more beautiful, because it's my country. Do you understand? Can anyone be so stupid as to carry out such a naïve comparison between home and exile? Have we reached that level of infatuation with the West?"

"Infatuation with the West?!"

You laughed in astonishment, your mirth stretching inexplicably on. Had my use of the term 'infatuation' – which I had stolen from my father – been so out of place? What a catastrophe! I began to feel as though I was in over my head and should never have embarked on such a discussion.

"My God! How good it is to hear such an opinion after eleven years!"

"I don't want to talk any more . . . !"

I looked down, trying in vain to follow the lines of my textbook. I bitterly wanted to cry. You smiled and patted my shoulder. A tremor travelled between us. I was bewildered. I loathed you so completely, so how could I explain the electric current quivering between us? Why did the mere thought of your hand on my shoulder make me tremble? I froze, afraid to look around. I heard your voice, full of pain and bitterness.

"You're cleverer than you look. But if you want my advice, don't go hunting for reasons. They won't be pretty. I can't give you easy answers. You'd do better to go back to your book."

Questions and tears welled inside me. How could you say such things about our country? Was Kuwait not the most wonderful place in the world?

And what did you know about Kuwait anyway? You did not love it. You had not chanted joyfully in Flag Square. You had not climbed the flagpole to hang our four-coloured banner aloft. You had not promised to die for Kuwait, to sacrifice your blood and soul for its sake. You had not carried arms to battle Arab soldiers as they came to seize your land, spreading tyranny under the pretence that "cutting necks is better than cutting livelihoods" and that they had come to liberate Jerusalem. You did not know what it was to sleep in a cellar, rocked by artillery as cries of "Allahu Akbar" rang from the mosques. You experienced none of that. The extent of your involvement was probably following the news on some radio. Had you even listened to it in Arabic, or had that been in Swedish too?

13

Sweet juice spread across my tongue, melting into water and sugar. Red liquid trickled down my throat, warm and fresh. I took another strawberry. Fields of strawberries stretched into the distance, covering every patch of ground in sight. I popped a large red fruit into my mouth, chewing hungrily. You were standing several feet from me, singing softly in your incomprehensible, but increasingly familiar, Swedish.

"Doesn't this trump all those boring trips?" you asked for the tenth time as though needing to reassure yourself of victory. You glanced at your watch.

"Time to leave the hall!" you called out with joyful ceremony.

My heart clenched and seemed to sink in my chest. I gazed up at the sky. You grew suddenly quiet, noticing my anxious eyes. I bit my lip nervously.

"Don't tell me you feel guilty for coming!" you cried impatiently.

"I never said that."

"So what's the problem?"

Eyebrows knitted, you buried your hands in your pockets, concealing your irritated trembling.

"Dhary, the Ministry of Education covered all the costs of sending me here so I could sit this exam," I stammered.

"But what difference will it make whether you've sat it or not?"

"Probably no difference at all."

"The Ministry knows that. Believe me."

"But what about my moral obligation to perform the duty I've been given?"

"Very nice, Little Mouse, this moral obligation of yours. If only you felt that way about other things!"

"Like what?"

Twisting your neck, you spat in disgust. "To hell with it!" you yelled, "What do they do to students over there? They've transformed you into a monster."

"Why are you yelling?"

"Do you drink blood plasma during *iftar*? And construct genetic codes instead of playing with Lego? Do you make fried eggs from the nucleus of a chick's cell? Do you cultivate bread mould in your fish tank?"

"Why are you being such an idiot?"

"&^%$#&%$#"[2]

"What are you saying?"

"&^%$#&)#@!%&"

"Stop it!"

You continued yelling in Swedish, kicking stones and heaving great sighs of frustration. You let out a stream of what I can only guess were curses. At that point, I lost control.

"Get away from me you stupid Swede!" I cried.

"I beg your pardon, ma'am, but don't forget yourself . . . I won't give you the honour of leaving."

My blood began to boil. I threw the basket of strawberries at you and ran to find a taxi. You continued to rant in Swedish while questions and tears welled within me.

"Hey! Where d'you think you're going?" you yelled, twenty paces away from me.

"I want to go back to Kuwait."

"Idiot!" Your voice shook with anger.

"Fool!"
"I cannot love a land that has insulted me so badly."
"What did Kuwait do to you?"
"Nothing! Nothing but refuse me citizenship."

14

A bidoun. That's what they call you. It means that you live without any official documents testifying to your existence, however stupid you may consider these bits of paper to be. It means that you can see the world but the world cannot see you. It means that you must rely on the hell that is others in order to get on in life, work and education. It means that, no matter what your level of learning, you cannot be employed so long as your employer requires a passport photo. It means that you must conceal your presence as you would a deficiency because you are an illegal alien in a country that you thought was your home. It means that you are booted onto the street as part of the Kuwaitization of the workforce. It means that you cannot progress beyond secondary education because university places are reserved for Kuwaiti students alone. You are forced to climb the ladder without using your hands. You cannot marry because official records are for nationals only. You cannot even divorce. How laughable the world is! Let us chant, calmly and earnestly: "Put an end to this nonsense now. Stop this country in its tracks."

"Dhary! You're a bidoun?" I asked, tears springing from my eyes. My limbs were trembling. I sank wearily onto my knees. Meanwhile, you dragged your feet sadly to the car, your proud head bowed for the first time.

15

I threw myself onto the back seat, crumpling into a chaotic heap. Pulling my knees to my chest, I lent my head against the cold window. It began to rain in Uppsala. Wonderful, spectacular rain. You were humming something that resembled tears. It was Sayyab's Rain Song, eternally and excruciatingly torn between fertility and pain: "And every year when earth turned green the hunger struck us". Numbing sadness descended over us. The desire to weep swelled within me while my fingers longed to scratch at something . . . The rain and your sudden raw emotion were more than I could bear.

You stopped the car at the side of the road and I did not resist. I didn't care. It was all the same to me. If the road had stretched on forever I would not have resisted. How strange it is that, in the midst of our sorrows, we feel suddenly safe and secure. I wanted to sleep . . . but what were the crows doing, wheeling above the street lamps? Did they not fear the rain?

You lowered the back window.

"Lean your head out," you ordered. How strange your voice sounded, as though I was hearing it for the first time. "It'll be a long time until you see rain like this again."

I leaned my neck out and let the water lick my forehead. Fat, round globules dropped down. You knew that for all Arabs rain was a kind of passion, for you were Bedouin at heart. Rolling the window up, I dried my face and faked innocent delight.

"It's wonderful!"

You smiled, filling your chest with air and exhaling a long sigh, as eloquent as any story.

"I would be able to tell Kuwaiti and Swedish rain apart even if blindfolded."

"Do you miss it, Dhary?" I asked, swallowing nervously.

"Madly."

Something inside me went out. I closed my eyes and felt fever rise within me, growing more mutinous and more indifferent with each passing minute.

From the author's novel *Irtitam lam Yusma' Lahu Dawii*
(A Soundless Collision),
published by Dar al-Mada, Damascus 2004.

Notes:
1 Literally meaning "God with good", it is a traditional greeting similar to the Bavarian "Gruss Gott" instead of "Good Day".
2 Angry, incomprehensible ranting in Swedish.

Fiction from **Kuwait**

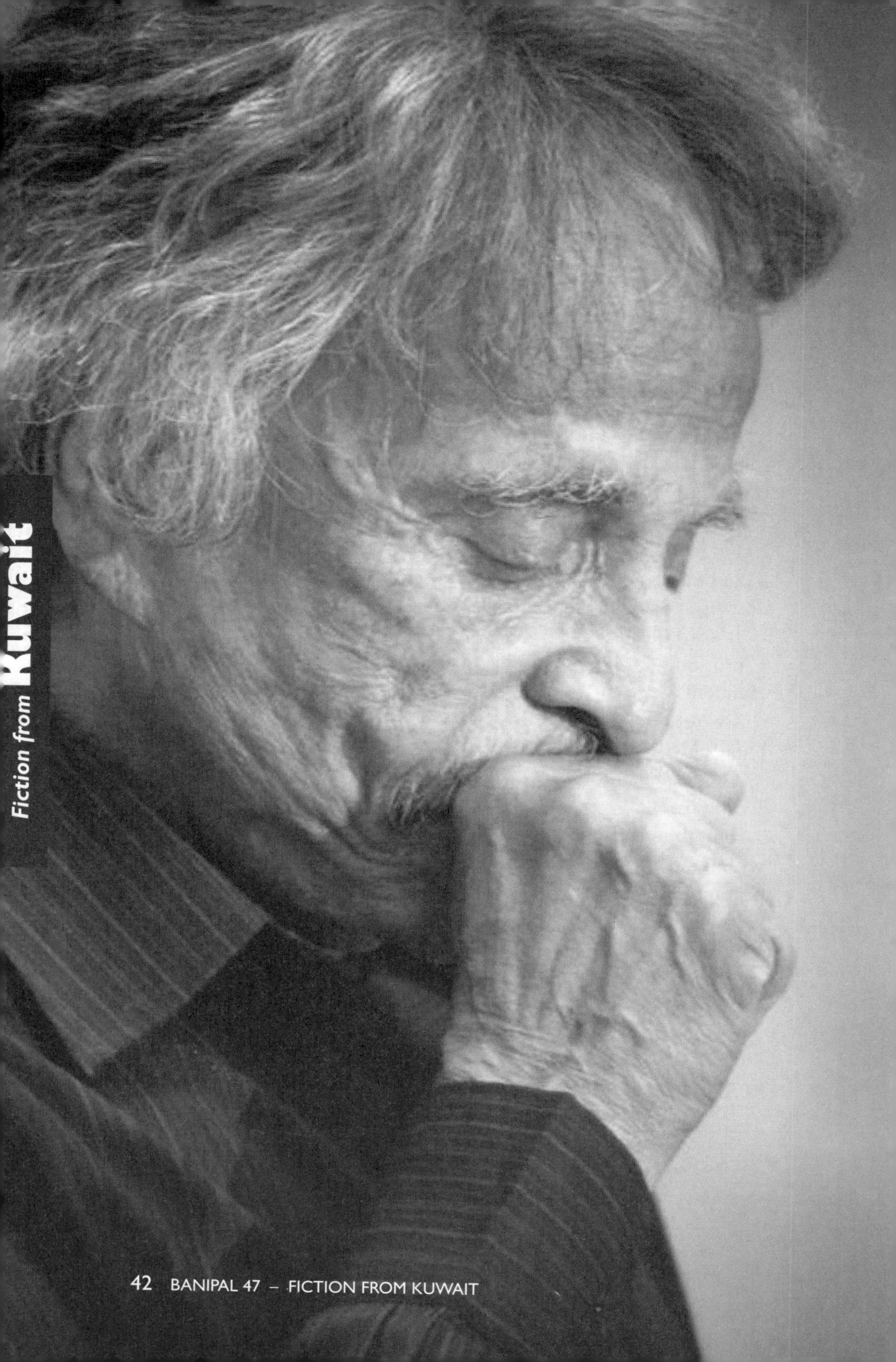
Fiction from Kuwait

ISMAIL FAHD ISMAIL

When the Frog Croacked

AN EXCERPT FROM A NOVEL,
TRANSLATED BY WILLIAM M HUTCHINS

Fiction from Kuwait

The taxi's headlights pierced the curtain of darkness that dominated the agricultural road leading from al-Ashar in the heart of Basra to the community of Abu al-Khasib. At this late hour of the winter night it was the only vehicle on the road. The windshield fogged up on the inside from their breath – his and the driver's – forcing the driver to wipe it clean from time to time with a special rag.

"It's a cold night!" Suleiman volunteered in an attempt to engage the driver in conversation.

"Indeed," the driver agreed tersely. He did not seem to have any desire to wade into an involved conversation.

"So be it!"

Countless plantations of date palms stretched into the distance, visible in the headlights just as giant trunks lining both sides of the road. He remembered covering the margins of his school notebooks with all kinds of drawings of date palms as a child. Man and the date palm originated in Basra, inseparably linked as a single community with a common destiny. When the taxi veered a little to one side as it wound across the giant wooden bridge over the river Hamdan, the memory of dense clusters of oleander bushes on either side of the road after the bridge burst into his mind's eye. He experienced a pure feeling of delight. The oleander bushes were still there. The seven years he had spent away from Iraq had not altered the landmarks.

"The intimacy of belonging to a place!"

Who said he had never been a child? He had once been one. He had been blessed with a wonderful aunt who lived there – behind a mass of palms, on the banks of the Hamdan itself. He had loved to visit her on Thursdays and stay over for Friday.

Time furnished excellent gifts, although it was true his aunt had died. All the same, that had happened long ago, and it was pointless to grieve now. The dark road twisted with successive curves that seemed like a challenge fraught with the savour of surprise. The oleanders were so dense they appeared ready to pounce, and the date palms . . . For as long as he could remember, drivers had been on the alert in this section of the Abu al-Khasib Road, for it contained seven switchback bends in less than a kilometre.

"A place for dreams!"

The idea of rolling down the window to smell the oleanders ran through his mind, but it was a winter night, and the driver was determined to remain silent.

"Never mind!"

His head was still full of his friends' words the moment he went to search for a taxi: "We'll meet again at the Hatif Coffeehouse."

"Eight o'clock tomorrow evening."

"We'll meet at the coffeehouse and then . . ."

"Tonight we've had to improvise. Tomorrow . . ."

"Don't you dare be late!"

He would have liked to tell them: "A longing for friends is comparable to a longing for family, but families have special rights . . ." In his case, his family consisted of his mother, father, brothers, and especially his little sister, who had been two when he left.

A separation of seven years while he was in Kuwait – who would believe that when he was proposing to purchase presents for each member of his family he had meant to get his sister a dress for a two-year-old girl? Fortunately, Najwa, who had insisted on accompanying him on his shopping trip, had had the presence of mind to object.

"You are ignoring the years that have passed!" she had said, displaying fond astonishment.

He had retorted: "Not on purpose."

That was over there; as for what had happened here . . .

"It's as if you had never left!"

Friendship enriched time and merged memory with the present.

"It seems we parted from you yesterday!"

When people meet – whether the separation has been long or limited – past and present join hands, framing the intervening period.

"Today belongs to my family."

"And tonight to us."

Their words, the entire conversation, was packed into his head, which was also wishing that Najwa had been able to accompany him on this trip home.

"Love has its own special time!"

* * *

"Where did you say?" The driver's morose voice brought him back to the present. He replayed those words, comprehending them, and responded with his own question: "You mean, where am I heading?"

The driver grumbled sullenly: "What else?"

The driver's glumness did not spoil Suleiman's splendid sense of delight. The celebratory time he was enjoying was too intense to be spoiled by transitory hostility.

"We'll be there in a few minutes," he said, to reassure the driver.

The other man snapped back: "We'll be there?"

His question had a provocative ring.

Suleiman, however, did not care to be provoked. So he explained in a tone he meant to sound amiable and calm: "Where I'm heading is the village of Bab al-Hawa."

"Bab al-Hawa?" the driver repeated this name as if it were an incomprehensible riddle.

A cunning smile formed on Suleiman's lips, and he explained further: "It's a small village connected to the village of al-Sabiliyat."

The riddle had only become more abstruse for the driver. "Al-Sabiliyat?"

Suleiman asked inquisitively: "Haven't you driven on the Abu al-Khasib road before?"

"I work the line between Basra and Amara." The driver's response revealed his nervousness as he continued: "I shouldn't have got messed up in this!"

Suleiman offered himself this justification for the driver's attitude: he's right – given that he's a stranger to this area.

Then he was surprised to hear the driver say: "If you don't mind," as if asking for permission. Without waiting for any sign of consent or disapproval from Suleiman, the driver trust a hand into an inside pocket, withdrawing a bottle, which he put it to his mouth to remove the cork with his teeth. When he spat out the cork, it rolled between his feet.

"What next!"

The scent of Mastaki arak permeated the taxi's closed atmosphere.

"To the health of your Bab al-Hawa (Gate of Passion)!"

The provocative tone of his voice seemed to lack the sting of sarcasm. He put the quarter litre bottle to his mouth and took a swig. He held his breath while savouring the stinging taste of the arak. He wiped his mouth with the sleeve of his dishdasha and carefully set the bottle down.

"So that's how it is then!"

* * *

He and the driver and the seven bends . . .

"What if the car . . ."

He kept one eye on the switchback bends while the other watched the interplay between the bottle and the hand holding it. He felt a mixture of dread and anxiety along with pangs of impetuous curiosity.

"Drink!"

The driver's unexpected invitation appeared half-hearted. The bottle remained near his own mouth.

"No, thank you."

If the driver had been a friend, he would have remonstrated: "You know I haven't drunk a drop since I left here!"

If the driver had been a friend, he would have burst out laughing and answered in a disproving tone: "What? Haven't you fallen off the wagon yet?"

He had been with them an hour ago, and they had pressed him to drink with them to celebrate his return. Would he be able to make them understand: "I no longer enjoy drinking"?

"You all know," Mustafa had said, soliciting the group's attention before he added as if stating a maxim, "Your comrade has . . . given that he has been living in Kuwait all these years, become . . ."

Their laughter increased.

" . . . a Hanbali bigot."

"Worse than that!"

Mustafa could say whatever he wanted, because he was hosting the party at his house, and his wife was right to warn them: "It's late! Don't forget he has a long ride home."

* * *

"What's the name?" This unexpected question burst from the driver. Suleiman was perplexed. The other man seemed to have been tuned to his thoughts.

"Whose?" he asked with astonishment.

The driver replied: "The village you said is connected to your Bab al-Hawa."

Suleiman's astonishment was accented by a pang of delight. Mutual disclosure was beautiful in a conversation.

"Has the arak achieved this quick effect or is it the enforced companionship?"

"Al-Sabiliyat."

The driver shared his opinion: "Weird name!"

He considered how to explain the meaning of the name, but his impulse to engage in banter – in that special setting – prompted him to say: "It actually is a weird name but is well-known among the residents of Basra and Amara as a whole."

Shaking his head in disbelief, the driver said quite seriously: "I haven't had the honour."

Suleiman continued in his bantering vein: "Every Friday morning, groups of buses travel to al-Sabiliyat with people from Basra or Amara who come to visit the tomb of al-Sayyid Rajab al-Rifa'i."

The driver put the bottle to his mouth to take another swig. Without wiping his mouth on his sleeve, he commented, while nodding his head unenthusiastically: "You don't say."

Suleiman still felt like kidding around. "Al-Sayyid Rajab, who is one of God's pious saints, is famed for his numerous miracles."

"You don't say."

The taxi passed the village of al-Sankar and approached the Habbaba Bridge. It would not be much farther. Should he tell the driver "Your gruelling mission is almost at an end"? Should he advise him, craftily steering the conversation in another direction . . .

"They all perform miracles . . . except for your friend . . ." the driver left the sentence unfinished.

Suleiman expressed his disbelief: "Our friend?"

"The short man." He fell silent briefly while searching for some epithet. "The stingy man who – I don't know how – found me on the street."

Suleiman caught his drift, remembering Mustafa, who had volunteered to find a taxi. His mouth opened into a broad smile. Meanwhile, the driver continued: "He convinced me the trip would take half an hour. When I asked for two dinars, he told me the usual fare was a quarter dinar, no more."

The taxi had almost arrived, and Suleiman was forced to interrupt and point. "There. That dirt lane!"

"We've arrived!" The driver slowed down. When the vehicle came to a stop, an clever idea popped into Suleiman's head: 'Why not?'

Gripping the door handle, he began to open it: "How much did Mustafa pay you?"

Astonishment blanketed the driver's face: "Mustafa?"

Suleiman explained: "Our short friend . . . the stingy man."

The driver, who had understood, moaned: "After all the toing and froing . . . he paid me half a dinar."

Suleiman was thinking: 'That being the case . . .' He did not finish his thought but instead thrust his hand in his pocket and pulled out two dinars: "If you'll allow me."

The other man vented his rejection and inebriation at the same time: "What's this?"

"The fare you justly requested."

The driver asked: "You think so?"

Suleiman replied resolutely: "Absolutely."

The driver, however, did not put out his hand to take the two dinars. He seemed to brood for some seconds. Then he asked a question that appeared to be spontaneous. "What's the name of the righteous man responsible for all miracles?"

Suleiman affirmed: "Al-Sayyid Rajab al-Rifa'i."

"And your's?"

"Perhaps this is an effect of the arak!" And since the driver was still waiting for a reply, he said: "My name is Suleiman."

The driver queried him: "Al-Rifa'i, as well?"

Suleiman grasped his meaning and chortled happily. "No," he replied. Then with genuine affection he added: "But you really deserve the two dinars."

For a second time the driver brooded for some seconds. "I'll take them on one condition," he declared decisively. Holding out the bottle, he said: " . . . that you join me in a drink!"

A form of short-term human bonding . . .

"Both of us being travellers."

Suleiman's answer was not spontaneous or premeditated: "The truth of the matter is . . . I don't drink."

"Keep your money then!"

"But . . ."

Although he had always pointedly refused to join his friends in drinking, this time he was forced by the taxi driver's stubborn refusal to yield.

"It's an emergency situation!"

* * *

Helping him take his suitcase from the boot, the driver said sympathetically: "Very heavy!"

Suleiman agreed resignedly: "It really is."

The driver asked sympathetically: "Is your house far?"

"A little way."

The driver's next comment was expressed wishfully: "If a car could drive down your lane . . ." He did not finish.

Suleiman replied: "Never mind."

He placed his right hand on the suitcase handle. Heavy as it was, he heaved it off the ground, steadied himself and started to walk.

"Bab al-Hawa – that's a pretty name," said the driver in parting. Suleiman did not know why he responded, without looking back: "Thanks."

* * *

It had been seven years since he left, but the lane linking the village of Bab al-Hawa with the Abu al-Khasib road had not changed. The fact that the village was virtually deserted may have played a part: only a few of the houses were still inhabited, after the mansion overlooking the Shatt al-Arab had lost its resident dozens of years earlier.

"Every time provides its own gifts!"

After the taxi and its headlights moved away, his eyes started to adjust to the dark. Then the features of the lane became clearer. Pangs of mournful homesickness stirred in his breast.

"My childhood and teenage years are linked to this place!"

The croaking of a solitary frog could be heard nearby. He was overwhelmed by an acute sense of familiarity. It had been seven years since he heard any frogs croak.

"Kuwait doesn't have any frogs!"

A second frog answered the first.

"Night has its voices!"

The numbness caused by the weight of his suitcase started in his palm and worked its way up his arm to his shoulder.

"It's not as easy as . . ."

He stopped and set the suitcase down. When he loosened his fingers from the handle, they tingled. He was suddenly gripped by a murky sense of foreboding.

"What's that?"

He turned spontaneously to his right, imagining that he had heard someone's heavy breathing. A scarcely perceptible tremor coursed through his body.

"What?"

He stared at the area he imagined to be the source. Among the palms, the darkness was even more intense.

"It's inconceivable!"

He sharpened his senses . . . especially his hearing. The frogs were croaking – that was all he could hear. He sighed with relief, switched hands to pick up the suitcase, and continued on his way.

"Night has its sounds!"

* * *

The lane would have felt comfortably familiar had he not felt apprehensive about some unexpected surprise.

"The house is straight ahead. I just need to keep walking."

The lane was familiar, but a bitter taste of being marginalized began to settle in his mouth.

"Like exile in a foreign land!"

For the second time in only a few hours, he was haunted by a strange sensation.

"If only Najwa were here!"

The first time had been when he was surprised to find Basra so unexpectedly congested with astonishing numbers of people – new people with different patterns of social interaction. "Post-revolutionary concepts . . ."

Responding to his analysis of the apparent change, Mustafa had told him: "You're like the Seven Sleepers of Ephesus – Ahl al-Kahf." He explained further: "Because you've spent all those years cut off there. Conditions have changed from what they were in your day."

He understood that conditions differed from when he had left in 1953. He knew that the revolution that had toppled the monarchy was still producing profound and rapid changes – expected and unexpected. "A year of change." Even so, he could not discover through his internal debate any logical or fantastical explanation for his deep-seated sense of estrangement from familiar things.

"Perhaps it's me!"

During his days in Kuwait, during the moments when homesickness roiled him, the image of this lane rather than of any other place had haunted him, dominating his entire memory. Early one autumn morning when the sky was crowded with grey clouds, the small stream with tributary creeks on both sides swelled to its banks with flood water. The palm fronds responded to the gale, and at that moment the rain had come down in torrents. "That's a beautiful memory of a scene, like an Impressionist painting," Najwa had commented when he had shared his homesickness with her.

"Maybe." He had agreed with her at the time but with one caveat. "It's just that whenever I search for myself in that scene, each time I find that I'm a child of six, alone, smitten with a burgeoning foreboding mixed with inchoate fear. I'm carrying a school satchel, which contains no books, and heading toward the primary school in a neighbouring village to enrol as a pupil for the first time in my life."

Najwa had said: "Perhaps homesickness takes you to this scene because you were forced to face something totally unknown to you – school."

He had agreed: "Perhaps."

In that context, there had been no need to inform her that "the neighbouring village where the school was located was al-Sabiliyat".

He had not needed to add: "Although I was extremely hungry at school that day, I didn't regret refusing to eat the breakfast my mother had made for me, because a boy of six doesn't understand the meaning of regret. But when I walked home at noon, I raced to the kitchen. Lunch wasn't ready yet. So I hurried to the date larder."

Some months earlier in Kuwait, he had received one of the letters his brother had written on behalf of their father. The letter included the statement: "The Agriculture Ministry's Date Palm Board has leased the mansion's outbuildings, which were used as horse stables in the days of the Pasha, to turn them into date warehouses." His father had seized this opportunity and applied for a job. The Board had offered him a position as a guard.

"Each time provides its special gifts."

* * *

His left arm was almost paralyzed. The numbness had extended to his shoulder and was honing in on his neck.

"This suitcase!"

He was certain it had become heavier. He stopped and placed it on the ground. He loosened his fingers, which were cramped round the handle.

"They're waiting for me!"

Renewed desire overpowered his suffering and fatigue.

"Even if they're asleep, I have the spare key. I'll open the door quietly and go in. In the morning they'll find me among them. That'll be a surprise . . ."

He did not complete the thought. A murky, anxious foreboding pervaded him again.

"Inconceivable!"

Suddenly he turned spontaneously to his right, sensing that someone was lying in wait for him there. His eyes were better adjusted to the darkness now. He stared.

"Nothing!"

There was no trace of anyone. The trunks of the date palms stood close to each other, and the understory trees that were scattered between them only added to the darkness.

"The frogs have stopped croaking!"

He listened intently. There was no sound — nothing to confirm his feeling of being watched. Was his sensitivity linked to living for years in Kuwait where there were no palm plantations and no bending agricultural roads? He switched hands to carry his suitcase.

"It's not far at all to the house!"

* * *

He heard dogs barking.

"Human habitation is close!"

He spontaneously quickened his pace.

"It's only a little farther!"

Once he reached the next bend, he would see the only entry to Bab al-Hawa: the *darwaza*.

There were quite a few of these darwazas in Kuwait: giant wooden gates, which one might call a cultural tradition. They were intended to serve as entrances in the wall that once encircled Kuwait City.

The darwazas there have their own special names, but the one in Bab al-Hawa is called "the darwaza", with its own definite article. Since Suleiman had left home, the residents of Bab al-Hawa and the neighbouring villages had reached a consensus about this name.

The narrow farm lane, which appeared to have rammed by force through the palm plantations, suddenly opened out after the next turning into an expansive open space free of trees. This area was divided in half by a mud brick wall with one three-metre wide opening. On either side of it rose the dilapidated remains of two historic towers built of fired bricks.

Suleiman remembered that, when he was a child, he and his friends had tried to scale one of these towers, but his father had seen them and shouted at him: "Get down!"

"I'm just playing," he had offered by way of an excuse.

His father's response was: "Playing like that is wrong!"

He also remembered that once when he was a young man and passing through this opening with his father, his father had commented mournfully: "The towers, which look so pathetic today, were once staffed with a strong force of guards around the clock."

Sounding increasingly regretful, he had added: "I was one of the men who took turns standing guard here."

Fiction from Kuwait

On joining the Pasha's service as a young man, his father had worked as a guard at the darwaza. Now that he was an old man, he was a guard at the date warehouse in the former stables of the Pasha.

* * *

The turning . . . here was the *darwaza*, only a few paces away.
"At last!"
He sighed with relief. Since this patch of earth lacked trees, he could see more clearly. He was filled with delight. Just as soon as he traversed that open space he would be in Bab al-Hawa.
"How can mere names have such emotional force?"
He forgot how heavy his suitcase was. The mud brick wall was unchanged . . . the damaged towers . . .
"They're as high as I remember them."
The walls cast their dark shadow over the interior space of the corridor through the *darwaza*.
"Things are just the same – as if these seven years had not . . ."
In a few minutes he would be home, but the sense of being watched came back, assailing him even more powerfully than the two previous times.
"Impossible!"
He said this to himself resolutely and decided that he would not stop to look to his right. The moment he approached the halfway point along the passageway, he imagined that the shadow cast by one of the two towers was separating itself from the tower – producing the spectre of a man.
"What is the meaning of this?"
He did not have time to investigate.
"Halt!"
The truncated, muffled command assaulted his ears. The mouth of a machine gun was pointed at the space between his eyes.

Selected from the novel *Yahduthu Ams* (Happening Yesterday),
Dar Al Mada, Nicosia, Damascus and Beirut, 1997

YOUSEF KHALIFA

18 Very Short Stories

TRANSLATED BY AGNES REEVE

Fiction from **Kuwait**

A PAINFUL REALITY

"Dad, is it true that Mums and Dads are supposed to sleep in the same room?"

"Yes, my daughter."

"So why do you sleep with that strange woman* and not with Mama Mary?"

AN EDUCATION

Honesty is better than dishonesty and telling the truth is a virtue. That is what the boy learnt at school today. But when he went up to his father and said "Dad, I broke my new toy today by accident," he found himself returned to his room with a swollen cheek.

AN EXPLANATION

She saw a scrap of paper next to her, so she picked it up and threw it in the bin.

No-one paid any attention.

A child tripped over in front of her, so she helped him up and wiped his face. She held out her hand to help a woman with a pushchair pass her on the pavement.

No-one paid any attention.

But when she walked hand in hand with her boyfriend, whom she'd been waiting for, everyone stared at her and their eyes were screaming . . . "Prostitute!".

DIFFERENT

When he climaxed, he embraced her, caressed her and whispered in her ear.

Worried, she telephoned her mother the next morning.

CONFUSION

For a long time, he was confused as to why sex seemed new and different every time his wife returned from her weekly visit to friends.

RESPECTING THE WIFE

In a dark room, under the covers, he quickly planted his seed in his wife and then instantly went to sleep.

In a room with different lighting, with music and dancing, he looked long into the eyes of the woman kneeling between his legs and igniting his passion – his mistress.

A BEATING

The father beat the mother, nobody moved.
The boy beat his sister and the father beat him.
The boy was confused.

A CONCEPT

A foreigner asked an Arab: "Tell me about freedom in your country."

"In my country I have complete freedom to say whatever I want and about whomever I want. Except about the Governor, and Vice-Governor, and officials, and religious leaders, and . . . and . . . etc."

A BLACK COMEDY

He took his seat in the theatre with his friend – it had been a long time since he had attended a comedy. When the curtain went up and he prepared to have a laugh, he saw his girlfriend in the audience with another man.

A FEELING

After twenty years of being a wife, and a mother to five children, a man looked at her from afar and smiled. And she remembered she was a woman.

Fiction from **Kuwait**

TWO LOVERS

She asked him: "If I give you my heart, my body, my soul, what are you going to give me?"

"Hmm . . . what do you think about this expensive watch?" he answered.

A DECISION

After three days of Arab delegations, meetings, compromises, appeasements, the spokesman revealed the final decision: "The State has chosen . . . to host the first Arab world singing festival!"

AN OFFICIAL

He took to the podium to give his speech. He cleared his throat and the audience started applauding. "Distinguished guests," he began, and they started applauding even more. Then he accidentally farted, and received a standing ovation.

DEMOCRACY

"I've heard that you're going to be holding elections following the death of the Governor last month. How many parties do you have?"

"Well, just the ruling party."

WATER IS SCARCE

The official declared: "Yes, I support the Minister and the Government in all their decisions. So therefore I urge you to remember . . . water . . . water . . . water!"

Later that evening, he slapped his houseboy across the face because he hadn't changed the swimming pool water for two days!

A REFLECTION

A woman and a man crossed paths.

The woman said: "How handsome he is . . . those glasses make him look really intellectual . . . and he's dressed so smartly . . . I feel like he has a strong character."

"Wow, what a great pair of . . . ," said the man.

AN ARAB LAW

"Dad, I've bought a painting that they say shows the face of the Prophet."

"God bless you, son, hang it to the left of the portrait of the Governor."

MODERN LIFE

He hadn't seen his mobile phone all day . . .

He felt a suffocating solitude . . . s.u.f.f.o.c.a.t.i.n.g. . . . S.U.F.F.O.C.A.T.I.N.G.

Note:
* This refers to a Filipino nanny

Selected and translated from the author's collection *Afkar Ariya* (Naked Thoughts) published by Dar al-Farabi, Beirut 2007

LAILA AL-OTHMAN

Two Short Stories

THE ABAYA OF AL-KADHIM
TRANSLATED BY RUTH AHMEDZAI

THE EID BISHT
TRANSLATED BY SALLY GOMAA

The Abaya of al-Kadhim

We were crossing the road between the palm trees and the sea, the rustle of the waves reaching out softly to us. His arm clasped mine offering me tender warmth, but it didn't prevent a shiver at the touch of a cold breeze. Sensing I was chilly, he withdrew his arm to take off his brown abaya, and wrapped it around me.

"Here, have my favourite abaya." he said.

This stirred my curiosity. "Is it very dear to you, then?" I asked.

He let out a long sigh: "It's so dear to me that I'm a prisoner to it."

I felt a pang of jealousy in my breast, but the warmth the abaya lavished on me kept it from stirring. It gave off an aroma, was a whisper of reassurance I had rarely felt in the years I had lived without love.

He let out a sigh that seemed somewhat excessive to me, coming from deep within his chest rather than his lips.

"What's wrong?" I asked.

He stopped. Taking my cold face in his warm hands, he looked at me, deep in thought, and whispered: "Would it hurt you if I spoke about an old love?"

His question took me by surprise and I was annoyed that just as he had given me warmth he let the cold seep back into every joint. I sensed the abaya was in some way linked with this old love of his and so I replied, struggling to contain my jealousy: "I don't need to hear about your past. I'm the one you love now."

He squeezed my arm, which I took as sufficient apology. The shudder of cold passed. I leant my head on his shoulder and felt myself being washed over by a wave that carried the sounds of fish sighing and the chatter of shells.

When we got into his car, he turned his whole body to face me. Looking at me fondly, he whispered: "I'd like to tell you what's weighing on my mind."

This made me feel apprehensive: "Has your bitter past still not left you? I thought my love had swept away things from the past, including the bitterness."

He fondled his abaya, which was still wrapped around me. As his

Fiction from **Kuwait**

hand stroked it playfully up and down, I imagined him caressing his former love. But his response allayed my suspicions: "I trust you'll take good care of it and that it will take good care of you, too."

He took me home. I wanted to take the abaya off, but he stopped me: "I want it to sleep with you tonight and for it to reveal to you what you wouldn't let me say."

He planted a soft kiss on my hand and wished me good night.

I put on my blue pyjamas, the ones he had given me. Wrapping myself in the abaya, I lay in bed. The smell of perfume wafted from it, stealing from my eyes their craving for sleep. Rustling like a whisper, its gilded embroidered edges chafed my delicate skin like his insatiable fingers, drawing maps of burning desire on my body.

How could I sleep? What kind of night did he want me, a prisoner of insomnia, to have? What was the secret lurking in this abaya? Had it touched the body of his former love? I sniffed it, hoping to detect the scent of a woman I didn't know, but instead was hit by a torrent of other smells, which reminded me of something I had once smelled on an old abaya. I was transported back to a distant memory and the voice of my Iraqi friend trying to cheer me up: "We'll visit the shrine of Imam Musa al-Kadhim to bless you and free you from this weight on your shoulders."

She knew I was flailing about in the dregs of that relationship. I was still smarting from the blow, struggling with that smouldering question, which refused to let the embers cool — "Why did he leave me and abandon me to such bitter cold and burning heat?"

I had given in to my friend and found myself whispering secretly to myself: 'Who knows? Maybe she's right. Maybe this visit will help me shake off this burden.'

The whole way to Baghdad, his disdainful image haunted me, trampling on my feelings. My heart was palpitating, on fire: 'Oh, if only he'd get out of my heart and let this fire die down once and for all!'

We arrived at the courtyard surrounding the sacred shrine. I stood there gazing at the beautiful building and the waves of breathless humanity scurrying to the entrance, laden with all their provisions, children, and the faith that al-Kadhim would intercede. We entered the colonnaded courtyard leading to the shrine. Just as I was about to enter, I was startled by a shout directed at me. "Stop!" the guard had commanded. "You can't enter without an abaya."

I had glared at him with contempt: "I hate abayas. I never wear them."

Visibly unimpressed, he didn't answer. He pulled one out from a pile in an old chest and instructed me to put it on. I recoiled in disgust. It was threadbare, the edges tinged with green from age and frequent use. A repulsive smell wafted from it, as if it had been steeped in the scent of the thousands of menstruating women, nursing mothers and licentious harlots, all of whom had worn it before me. Putting it on, I felt as if I carried on my shoulders all their woes, their odours and perhaps their sins, too. I flung it off again, clinging to my friend in defiance: "I don't want al-Kadhim's blessing."

She cautioned me with a pinch: "Hey! Watch what you're saying!"

She picked up the abaya and pulled it down over my head, then pushed me from behind towards the entrance to the shrine. With difficulty we squeezed our way through the crowds. All around, I could hear prayers for al-Kadhim's blessing and women wailing with the howling of injured souls. Their mingled voices flooded my ears with the poison of their humiliation, the pus of their festering wounds and the intimate details of their various hardships and I was filled with a strange sorrow, as though some narcotic was oozing through me, numbing my limbs. But then, suddenly, I found myself squeezing through a narrow gap between two women, and my forehead pressed against the iron railing surrounding the tomb. At that moment, as my bitter memories piled up on top of me all, my pain came flooding back. Overwhelmed by despair, my tears streamed down and a gasping sob seemed to well up and break free from deep within my chest. My friend's voice burst in on me and commanded: "Pray to al-Kadhim and ask for his help. He will not let you down."

This insistence that I should beg for help brought back painful emotions from the past. I pictured myself after my beloved, that bastard, had left me . . . sprawled out on my prayer mat, rubbing my tear-stained face and clawing at my humiliated breast, beseeching God: "Oh Lord, take him from my heart just as You took him from my path."

But there he remained. To that day, when I stood before the tomb of al-Kadhim, he had never for a moment stopped menacing my heart. Was it really possible I could rid myself of this torture as my friend insisted?

My head was spinning and I felt nauseous from the multitude of

Fiction from Kuwait

people, the smells, and the grief of womankind that was crammed into every thread of the fabric of the abaya. My feet could no longer bear the weight of my sorrow and the lashing blows of these memories. As I toppled to the ground, my friend's arms embraced me and she let out an anxious gasp. As she tried to support me, my body felt heavy and it seemed as if that man, my beloved, was looming over me with all his cruelty. But she managed to get me on my feet and helped me to leave the shrine with me still in fits of tears.

A cold breeze brushed by me, relief from the cloying heat of that crowded space. I had to free myself from this suffocating abaya. I pulled the hateful thing off and flung it away, wishing it would burst into flames and burn away the pain of every woman who had worn it. We walked to my friend's car, which was parked nearby. My sobs were still welling up within me; my gasps were like knives lacerating my ribs and searing my flesh.

When I was sitting in the car, she turned to me, anxious to calm me down and sprinkle a little hope: "Your tears have cleansed your soul. The blessing of al-Kadhim will not fail you." Seeing my eyes betray a flash of doubt, she tried to reassure me: "Trust me . . . You will sleep peacefully tonight."

It was years before that evil man was gone from my heart. I didn't count on ever tasting love again, assuming that the state of mind that had taken hold of me would keep me captive forever, but a glowing dawn did indeed arise and open up beautiful new vistas when life once again brought me love.

And here I was, embraced by his abaya, evoking the old aromas of al-Kadhim's shrine. I took a deep breath of the fragrant air and breathed out a whisper of a prayer: "Oh Lord, open my path up to him just as you opened up to him my heart."

I buried myself in his abaya, rubbing it all over my body. I smothered it in hundreds of kisses, before sleep trickled into my eyes and I slipped into the caverns of dreams.

In the morning, I expected him to call, eager to ask whether the abaya had unfurled its secrets as he had hoped. But he didn't call. While my phone was persistent, his remained switched off. Anxiety opened the gates to the worst suspicions, which scratched away at me with their talons. I decided that the only way to fight them was to go to his house.

I put on the red suit he loved and did my hair in his favourite style. I picked some jasmine flowers for him and set off, driving even faster than the ridiculous speed of the other cars.

When I turned into their street I was shocked to see swarms of women swathed in abayas going in and out of his house. Who could have died? His mother? One of his sisters? Or . . . ?!

I could hear the voices of the women passing by the car, muttering: "May he rest in peace and God's mercy" and urging his mother to find patience and consolation. The news pounced on me, utterly without mercy. I closed the car window and let out a resounding scream, my heart howling in pain: "Was he saying goodbye yesterday as he gave me his abaya? Did my prayers get lost on the way to heaven? Is that what's closed off my path to him and instead brought only agony to my heart?"

I couldn't go in dressed as I was. I turned away, not knowing where I could go with my pain. There was no space broad enough for my screams and no well deep enough for my tears. I went home and was surprised to find my mother in distress. Before she could say anything, I threw myself on her chest, howling.

"His sister rang and told me the news . . ." she said, her voice shaken by tears. "Where have you been?"

"I went to see him and that's where I found out."

She pushed me away, horrified: "Dressed like that?"

"I found out before I went in."

"We must go there right away," said my mother.

We put on our abayas and left.

I threw myself into the lap of his mother, who had loved me and betrothed her son to me. I wept, unable to utter a single word of condolence. I needed someone to console me and lessen the weight of my loss. Her hand was on my head, rubbing away her torment, and her wailing voice scratched through my skin, spilling acid inside me: "He let al-Kadhim's blessing go to waste . . . and he himself has gone to waste . . . We've searched everywhere for his abaya to wrap his body in, but we can't find it."

The question hit me like a convulsion: 'Has he also got some link with al-Kadhim?' I didn't dare admit that I had his abaya, fearing the assault of his mother's grief if she imagined that I had had some hand in his death.

I didn't sleep that night. I couldn't bear to be in my soft, warm bed while he was lying in the dark earth. And besides my grief, I was driven to distraction by the mystery of the abaya: 'What was it he hoped I might learn from it? Why did I stop him and waste his chance to reveal it to me? How can I find out this secret?'

I needed to know. I went to my mother's room. She was performing the dawn prayer and her face was weary. Her cheeks were trailed with tears, still flowing though her eyes were closed. I waited until she had finished her prayer and wiped her face with her palms, then threw myself on her knees. I was in floods of tears.

"What's all this about the abaya?" I asked her.

"Do you really not know?" she said, astonishment palpable in her voice.

I slapped my cheeks, burning with distress. "Only yesterday he wanted to tell me something and I didn't let him. This is agony . . . agony . . ."

She stroked my head, praying to God to give me patience before she told me the story.

I learnt the mystery of the abaya. I learnt the secret of his former love, a woman who had loved him so passionately that she had tormented him until he was on the brink of madness. His mother was gripped by the idea that this woman had bewitched him. She was afraid for him, so she took him to Baghdad, where she bought him the abaya and took him to al-Kadhim for him to be freed from her magic spell. She wiped every inch of the abaya against the tomb and then placed it on him, making him swear never to take it off or to lose it.

'But in a moment of love he had forgotten to heed her words. Perhaps he gave me the abaya because he didn't believe what his mother had done to break the spell and its consequences. And me? Do I really believe this is why he's gone?'

I was afraid of the abaya. I looked at it, strewn across the bed, and felt that every thread was imbued with devilish intent, as though it had a thousand eyes pelting me with stones on behalf of the woman he had spurned.

A shiver ran through me as I walked over and grabbed it. I began to fold it tenderly, scattering within it the remains of my shattered dreams. I waited until daybreak, then took it with me as I headed to the sea.

I buried myself in my grief, mixing the salt of my tears with that of the sand. I held the abaya close to my chest, wishing I could tear myself open and bury it in my heart. I kissed it. I moistened it with the torment of my loss. I offered it my condolences. Prevailing over the scent of the sea and the sand was the overpowering aroma of the women of al-Kadhim, wounded like me, which billowed from the abaya along with the dust and everything else it had picked up along the way throughout its painful history. I hesitated, confused.

'Should I keep it as a memory to warm myself every time my heart is ravaged by a storm of longing for him? Or perhaps if I keep it, it will always reignite my smouldering grief and besiege me with remorse, because I obeyed him and took his abaya?'

I stepped into the sea. I washed the abaya. I screwed it up into a ball. I hugged it with all my love and my pain. I kissed it with all the kisses that I longed to give him. Then I wiped my tears with it, blessed it with my prayer, and sent it off swaying gently on the crest of a wave.

The Eid Bisht[1]

That afternoon, my father set off for his real estate office as usual. He always came home in the evenings after the evening prayer, but if he had errands to run, he would let my mother know beforehand so she would not worry. After carefully locking the door, soft echoes of her daily prayers would reach my ears: "May God save you and grant you great wealth and good fortune." Filled with contentment, she would turn and go back inside the house.

But that day she walked heavily, dark clouds circling her face. Maybe she had some reason to be upset with my father, I thought to myself. The words rushed out of my mouth: "What's wrong, Mother?"

She ran her tongue over dry lips. The edges of her words were dulled with apprehension. "Your father did not tell me where he was going tonight after the evening prayer." Despite sensing the fire burning within her, I pretended to blame her: "But you didn't ask him?!" She seemed genuinely puzzled for a second before responding: "I've never had to ask; he always told me. But why didn't he today?"

She tried to swallow her question and her pain. But they stuck in my own throat like a thorn.

My father did not come home after the prayers and my heartbroken mother spent the whole evening in her usual spot on the cotton-covered sofa in the courtyard. I was watching her from my bedroom window. She would either lie down or try to keep busy by mending the loose hem of one of my dresses. Between her sighs, she implored God in a trembling voice: "Why didn't he tell me

The Arabic cover of the short story collection A'ba't al-Maqam

this time?" The question cut through her like a sharp knife.

Then for a while, she turned quiet as if fast asleep. When she woke up, she started humming her favourite tune, the one she had learned on her wedding night long ago. Her voice was barely audible, remote as if coming from a deep well within her soul. My heart went out to her, seeing how tormented she was as she desperately tried to figure out a reason why my father was keeping secrets from her.

I went out to join her.

When I sat next to her, I noticed her cheeks glistening with tears. I looked at the hem of my dress and saw that it had not been mended. It was then that I began to fathom the depth of the sorrows that had engulfed her like bottomless seas.

I gently pulled the dress away from her. "Let me take it, Mother. I'll do it." She did not resist. She drew her legs to her bony chest, wrapped her arms around her knees, and let her head hang over them. Her thin braids fell, one on each side of her shoulders.

I started to sew, switching my eyes between the dress and my mother's pale face, which was distorted by the growing number of her unanswered questions. When the lamp in the liwan[2] cast its light over her face, the lines around her forehead and her chin looked deeper, making her look older than when my father had left in the afternoon.

To break the silence, I asked, trying to sound casual: "So where do you think my father is off to?" She sighed, and, raising her eyes to the sky, said in a tearful voice: "God knows. But I'm terribly worried about him." I tried to make up some excuse to calm her down: "Maybe he's having dinner at someone's house nearby." For a moment, her face lit up, but doubt quickly found its way back to her heart and she retorted crossly: "Why didn't he tell me then?" "Maybe he forgot," I said to console her. "Maybe." But she sounded more resigned than convinced.

She remained quiet afterwards, assailed by fears if not by suspicions. I resumed my sewing, the needle piercing my finger every time I tried to steal a look at her.

Our silence was interrupted with a loud banging on the iron door. I sensed her cringing as if hit by something hard. We both panicked because my father always used his keys. Who could it be? Had something bad happened to my father?

With a gesture of her hand my mother urged me to open the door. I shook with anticipation as I ran to find out who the caller was.

It was Hassan from my father's office. I was relieved to see nothing alarming on his face: "What's up, Hassan?"

"Uncle needs his bisht," he said looking down as he always did.

When I told my mother what Hassan wanted, it shocked me to see her gasp as if her throat had been cut open before she burst out crying. "Why did you have to do this?" she asked faintly between her tears.

She was only in her room for a moment before emerging with the bisht folded and wrapped in a white towel and held in her outstretched arms like the small body of a dead child at a funeral. She passed it to me and burst out crying again. When I held it, it smelt like stale perfume. As I handed it over to Hassan, I paused for a second. I wanted to ask him about my father's whereabouts. But he snatched the bisht out of my hands and left hurriedly to avoid any questions I might ask.

I went back to my mother. She was standing up, tense, eager to receive any information to calm her fears. When I did not utter a word, she fired questions at me all at once: "Did you ask him where

Fiction from Kuwait

your father was? Where was he eating? Why did he ask for the bisht?" I responded to her sheepishly, pretending to apologize: "Oh dear, it didn't cross my mind to ask, and Hassan was in such a hurry."

She fell to the floor as if pulled down by an invisible force. She rubbed her dry hands together. They made a hissing noise. Her voice was now stripped of confidence: "Lord, please do not destroy me; please do not break my heart."

I did not understand the meaning of her urgent plea, or the reason behind my father's absence that night. I could not muster the courage to ask her for an explanation even when she asked me to sleep next to her in the same spot my father usually occupied.

She never fell asleep. She spent the night crying, vacant-eyed and broken-hearted.

On the following day, before noon prayers, my father showed up. He stood in the middle of the courtyard and called out for my mother. She walked out to meet him with small, hesitant steps.

Hiding behind my bedroom window, I saw him take a gold necklace from his pocket. He tried to put it around her neck. But she recoiled from his touch, sobbing wildly like a grief-stricken mother. He tried to hold her back and I heard him begging her to stop crying and calm down. But she escaped his grip and ran to her bedroom. She banged the door so hard behind her as if trying to break it.

My father left the house quickly, as if someone was chasing him.

I immediately went into my mother's room. Her hair was wild. Her dress was torn open down the middle, revealing two sagging breasts. She looked broken, bewildered, bereft, incessantly wailing and chattering incomprehensibly as if out of her mind.

Since that day, my father has been spending one night at our house, and one night at his new wife's house.

Selected from the authors' collection *A'ba't al-Maqam*
(Abaya of the Shrine) published by Arab Scentific Publishers,
Beirut 2012

Notes:
1 A *bisht* is a ceremonial abaya worn by men on special occasions
2 *Liwan* is an ancient term meaning a central open space or courtyard in a traditional house.

ALI HUSSAIN AL-FELKAWI

Traveller of the World

EXCERPTS FROM A NOVEL
TRANSLATED BY THOMAS APLIN

They don't recognise me as the best tour operator because they don't understand the essence of what I do. I don't own a travel agency; I own the cities. Like the great conquerors I amass the world's heritage, from horses' hooves to computer monitors. Perhaps I exaggerate somewhat but who, before they were eighteen, has read works of those ancient travellers – the adventures of Ibn Battuta, the journeys of Ibn Jubayr, and the writings of Ibn Munqidh! Tour operators are not experts in anything. Some of them might own the plushest, the most opulent offices, but they don't know the compass points, and they know nothing of the "great travellers". But I am different. As soon as a city catches sight of me she emerges, almost as one, and embraces me with her eyes lowered. Or it could be said that she's sweet on me because I know and understand her history. I've read Maqdisi's *The Best Divisions for Knowledge of the Regions*, and Ibn Duqmaq's *The Pleasure of Humankind in the History of Islam*. Does your average travel agent know Ibn Duqmaq? Duqmaq, such a beautiful and mysterious name. I've tried it with my own name, Ghanim. When said out aloud it has a musical ring to it – "Ghanim al-Duqmaqi". So many books, volumes, dictionaries, treatises and names. For example there's Nasir Khusraw's *The Book of Travels*, Ibn Fadlullah al-'Umari's *Major Roads to Different Lands*, al-Maqrizi's *Topographical Description and History of Egypt*, and naturally, Yaqut al-Hamawi's *Dictionary of Countries*. Tens of books, tens . . . by geographers, travellers and historians moving through the imaginary time of historical events, who have observed vast expanses of time, have written them with their steps, and drawn them with their quaking breaths. I have walked the Silk Road with my bare feet in the footsteps of the first missionaries. On the same road I have hurried after the first mujahideen. Give me the name of one travel agent who has read and done all this. And even if you could count everything I've read, and all the distances I've travelled, I will never stop. I will continue to read and walk to the ends of the earth.

But never mind all that. I want those who refused to recognise me and held back their blessings to know that I have climbed the sand dunes of the first Orientalists, I have ridden the waves of those travellers who sailed the waters of the Arabian Gulf, and with the dust of caravans I have hastened to the Far East and into the depths of Africa. I became "westernized" until I happened across the books of the Orientalist Edward Said and concluded that Orientalism is also a form of tourism, but to the very depths of thought and the intellect. It is the joining of two opposites, or the intermingling of two foreign elements in storms of fire, kicked up by the hooves of a camel racing in the unknown. Except that I didn't really get Edward Said. Some will think me a second, or even third-rate intellectual. But never mind, I've delved deeply into contemporary travel literature; I'm even familiar with the work of the young Omani Mohamed Al-Harthy. Travel literature in Oman is as wide as the Arabian Sea. I've spent many an hour studying the contours of countries on Google Earth, and navigating the geography of the continents online. I've flayed the skin off my feet to walk hundreds of miles across thousands of gigabytes of web pages, wandering over rivers and steppe country; loitering in alleys and souks, beneath colossal bridges, and in metro tunnels. I've been to a million places in a single country, and in more than one era. A part of me grows in the places I visit, or a part of those places grows on my body.

. . .

Wealthy customers are a pleasure and pay up without asking too many questions. Even with the spread of online booking sites and the decline of the travel agency, a small number of well-to-do customers allow my establishment to turn a neat profit. On the other hand, those customers with a limited income continue to badger my employees without a profit in sight. The younger ones burst into my glass cubicle and bombard me with questions: Where is the best massage parlour in Bangkok? I want to go to Slovakia with my sick father. Where can I find a nightclub that's open at one in the morning? A week from now I'm going to see Barcelona play Athletico Madrid. Where are the best places to have a good time in Barcelona? How can I find Spanish women for company and dancing? Please don't get me wrong, but how many Euros is it a night? They often treat me as though I were a pimp! They don't value my love for the job, my professionalism. That's what really bothers me, although in the end I give them the answers they seek. What can I do? If one doesn't have a little bit of the pimp about him, then he won't only lose his customers, he'll lose his friends and maybe even his life too.

Business is good during the public holidays, especially the two Eids and the pilgrimage season. During those days, when the country is like a hot loaf draped in sheets of dust, business flourishes and sales rocket. This is especially so throughout July and August, when the entire population goes out and buys a suitcase the size of an airplane, a suitcase big enough for all. The people here travel together, they shop and they sleep together. It's as though they were born at the same time and will die at the same time. They are nothing more than carbon copies that merely transform themselves into more carbon copies. I, on the other hand, am transformed into an octopus. With one arm I give out forms, with another I answer the phone, and with tens of others I pick up fresh money. No sooner does September come around than business starts to quieten down and the tourists return to their roosts. Things pick up a little in October and November, and during December there's Christmas and New Year. Then there's the Spring break in February. After this, business is fairly steady until the summer migration begins anew. For me, my work is a little sacred. I like to see to my customers' every need. It's about more than tickets and hotel confirmations; I truly want them to have a good time. I dream, with them, of that magical step that will take them from the dream to the land where dreams are realised, so that they can return with beautiful memories. At a moment's notice, I can send them dollars via Western Union. I am their portable embassy, their adopted family. I share their joy and sometimes I even dance with them. I never cut the cord that connects our souls.

Tourism is sacred – steps taken between the feet of Buddha and the endless road to wisdom. The Peripatetics froze the limits of idealism and in so doing raised a ceiling on their sky, while the great capitalists, at the peak of their expansion, established luxury resorts, gleaming hotels and floating cities. Except that the greatness and power of tourism becomes apparent in how it drinks the sap of anyone who has spent his years doing nothing but work and squirreling away his money in bank vaults so that, in the end, he can fill a glass and raise a toast to travel.

Why, I wonder, why did Buddha cross all those distances to attain spiritual transformation? Neither the philosophy of the Peripatetics nor the account books of the capitalists have ever interested me to the same extent that humankind's desire to travel has perplexed me. Is travel another face of freedom? A synonym for humankind! Or is it just a pleasant escape? Is travel a hidden room in which we live out our secret fantasies? Is travel an intrinsic part of human nature? Perhaps we are searching for ourselves at the ends of the earth, or for another life that we believe is for us, or a life that can only be realised by a movement through time. Paul Bowles and the like are no longer the custodians of a traveller's time. Cyberspace has annulled the old distances between the traveller and the tourist. It has made places familiar and given a sense of the flow of time in the arteries of humanity. Now we live a shared vision. Everyone is free to associate with the landmarks and names of cities. Everyone is free to listen to the world's hidden stories, to know its most intimate secrets, to live any event he chooses through the eyes of one its characters. Everyone is free to lay his head on the chest of the city that pleases him. Yes, you are all free to engrave your immortality in the bark of a tree on the open road and move on, without even waiting for time. In those fleeting moments, when the creative soul merges with the gleam of material things, foreign fingers touch the farthest atoms at a single stroke. The word sparks and fire ignites without the need for anyone's permission or a decree from any being.

I always send out one of my employees with the tour groups – either Amin or Mustafa, or I coordinate with local tour guides. I also retain a head of sales, Melvino. This man of Indian origin is the real money-spinner. Three years ago he opened a branch of the company in India under the care of his nephew Capi, along with two wonderful representatives, Ibtisam and Marwa. In the afternoons, when there are no customers and a gentle, languid throb has crept its way along the edges of the body – the long and the short, I imagine a chaos of sexual relationships between the office workers. I conjure up scandalous pictures, or short chaotic, dirty movies where roles and bodies are swapped.

. . .

I wasn't expecting his visit, but naturally I was pleased to see him. Whenever his generous shoes trod my office floor it meant I would have no problem paying the rent or my employees' wages that month. I would be able to buy things that I had forgotten existed. Hamad Sultan Hamad was one of the middle-class well-to-do – his bank balance barely reached the four million dollar mark – but his generosity raised him to the ranks of the rich. I have tried to make him understand that I am the agency's proprietor, that I do not travel as a tour guide, and third, fourth and fifth, I do not like Europe. Specifically, I do not like the south of France, no matter how verdant it is, or how easy it is to lose oneself in its varied terrain. I like the cities of South East Asia: the riot of colours, the glitter and the sounds, and how the colour and the glitter reflects and is repeated upon the soul in a manifold concentration, lending the minute an extra age, and the age its serenity. If someone could weigh a minute in the resorts of Asia, such as Hua Hin and Sentosa, he would find it heavier by two days than a minute spent in the most luxurious European resorts. I wasn't going to agree to his proposition, of course I wasn't — until he handed me a cheque crowned with a figure that covered the office rent for two months and one hundred and fifty per cent of the workers' wages. I am not that materialistic, but it is my work and needs must. Who likes everything about his job? With these words I endorsed my almost complete submission before a piece of paper. The child and the fool do only as they like. Everything has its price, I added. Also, I am providing a service for a price.

I spent the entire day making such additions to sweeten the airs of my dignity until I began to wonder what the word "dignity" actually means. I decided it is a word that doesn't point to a specific meaning. It is a loose word, loaded with abstractions and false connotations. A semantic con, with roots sunk in wine. It is an unreasonable word; it lacks balance. In the end I concluded that there was nothing undignified about the relationship between the shoe and the nose on the one hand, and between the desire to refuse and urgent need on the other.

I dropped off the suitcases and collected the boarding passes — there were seven besides my own. After I had counted them and checked the names were correct, I looked over the dates of birth. Hamad was 56 years old, and his wife Ibtihal, 54. Their daughter Mona was 19 and their son Sultan 17. Aunt Najwa was 49 and her two daughters Hind and Hinadi were 18 and 16 respectively. I spent the remaining time before take-off chatting to colleagues and old friends, ground staff and workers in the airport administration, while I observed the excitement that spilled out with the movement of people between Arrivals and Departures. An hour before take-off, Hamad arrived with his family. I said goodbye to my friends and jumped.

The instant I set eyes on the huge head of Hamad's son, perfectly in proportion to his body, I realised just how a man's genes can degenerate and the branches of his ancestry weaken. Sultan bore none of his father's noble features or distinction, or the elegance and affability of the sons of the wealthy. Something in his eyes suggested a certain aggression and stupidity, and his reactions were slow and erratic.

"Sultan, Sultan," whispered his father and then, after failing to get his attention, he bellowed: "Sultan!"

A little after I made their acquaintance, I noticed the females had similarly narrow noses and thin lips, although, with the exception of these two traits, they were quite different. Each had a certain beauty with which she trumped the other. The girls held hands and strolled over to the Duty Free. Laughing, Sultan tried to prevent Mona from joining her two friends.

"Sultan, Sultan!" bellowed his father.

Ibtihal trembled as she drank her coffee. All the conversation of the previous half hour had revolved around her fear of flying. Aunt Najwa punctuated Ibtihal's trembling with firm nods of reassurance. With only a little time remaining before take-off, we took our seats at gate 21.

He pushed his knees into the back of Mona's chair.

"Sultan, Sultan!" bellowed his father.

I was captivated by Hamad's magnanimity, his sense of pride, his sincere love for his nearest and dearest, friends and acquaintances. I was fairly certain he was covering the travel costs for his aunt and her two daughters. But love and generosity are not just about paying for things; it's also about the way in which the money is paid. He paid me by cheque as though I were giving him the cheque. He could have booked me into economy, but instead he wanted to show me I was one of the family and booked me into business class with himself. What can I call all this – the morals of the rich? The rich, the rich and not the upstarts or the nouveau riche, regardless of the extent of their wealth. Those who are created rich can smell the authenticity of their souls, the purity of their conscience and the nobility of their character. Every time Hamad left the agency, the workers would mock his guileless generosity. They would dredge

Fiction from **Kuwait**

up their childhood misery and recall behind and in front of their eyes the tragic histories of their families: the screaming, the bitter resentment, the tears, the smashing of kitchen crockery over the heads of family members. They made him the murderer of their dreams, the destroyer of their aspirations, and Hamad would redouble his generosity because he wanted to improve the quality of our lives. What can I call all this? The magnanimity of the rich and the resentment of the poor!

Ibtihal rubbed her face against Hamad's shoulder like a cat and he squeezed her hand. This was all I could see from my corner. It seemed she couldn't bear take-off and was seized by a fit of anxiety, which, thankfully, fell short of full-blown hysteria. A stewardess quickly came over with a cup of water. She swallowed a Xanax and continuing to squeeze his hand, rested her head on his shoulder and was quiet. The girls sat behind us, nudging each other and whispering amongst themselves, while a couple of seats in front of us the aunt sat half asleep. Sultan sat beside her watching funny video clips on his mobile phone. The stewardess asked him to switch it off.

"Sultan, Sultan!" bellowed his father.

I saw Hamad, the father, his generosity and the way he watched over his little family, and I remembered my own angry father five years before. Even to this day, I am not sure whether it was the mop handle or a small hammer that just missed my head as I skidded towards the iron door. I slammed into the door with a crash – my skull is still vibrating from the impact. I don't like to remember these things, but they are stirred up whenever circumstances are to some extent similar. Such as, every time I board a plane, recalling the job I resigned from, where I worked as a senior steward – overseeing the preparation of passengers' meals, demonstrating safety instructions . . . If an acquaintance or relative happened to board – particularly those who have a boorish block of wood for a mind instead of an understanding and flexible mentality – we would quickly swap aisles with the steward who was related to the passenger. I was never embarrassed by my job, but my father and to some extent my sisters were. At the beginning, I felt like I was navigating the air with Sindbad and his princess Yasmina; or that I might fly with Alice to Wonderland – only, I would have got stuck in "the little rabbit-hole". But after a while I began to feel like a slave bound to the bow of a ship. There was no field in which I could live out my slavery; I was a temporal hostage at more than 30,000 feet. I said goodbye to Ibn Battuta and dismounted the horse of Ibn Munqidh and disembarked from the ship of Ibn Jubayr. Five years ago, I handed in my resignation, to escape work, to escape the house. Although I did not stray far from my milieu, I broke my chains and bought a travel agency. I have seen the world beneath my feet. In turbulent and stormy skies, I've heard brutish men whimper and women scream. During emergency landings and violent storms, I have listened to them with contempt while they have begged and asked God for forgiveness. I have slipped nimbly between the fingers of death, offering water, pillows and smiles beneath a downpour of mini apocalypses. They tried to court my favour, to catch my smile, so they would feel safe – will we be saved? The plane landed.

I stretched out my arms as far as I could. I don't know when or where I acquired this habit. Groggily, I found myself drawn to the white statues atop misty peaks. Always, as soon as the plane doors opened I would emerge either into the air bridge or onto the naked horizon and take in deep breaths, chasing out the stagnant air in successive exhalations, and I would open out my arms. I looked at my group: Gulf Arab elegance, coordinated colours and steps, with the exception of Sultan, of course. Everything was going according to plan. We would spend two nights in Paris and then travel by train to the south of France.

The reactions of my companions didn't reflect the magic of Paris, it was just another tourist city. The first night was gloomy for those who were used to sleeping in their own rooms without sensing the monotony of the night or its passing beneath their eyelids in an indiscernible colour; for those who were used to waking in the morning without wondering if the stars had failed to shine the previous night. I haven't felt any homesickness since I travelled the length of France three years ago. Cities are fond of me. I understand them and their history – from the time when they were merely forest or ancient reed beds. I am an acquaintance of distances. We returned to the hotel and I immediately set about revising the trip's itinerary.

In the morning, refreshed and invigorated, we toured the sites. Even Sultan let out a giggle from beneath the fuzz of his moustache. I was sure this must have been the first time he had quivered with excitement – almost. I entered into the spirit of things with a smile and joined in the family chatter. Even the cautious aunt, in a moment between happiness and sadness, pointed to her two daughters busily snapping photographs around the Eiffel Tower and whispered to her sister: "I wish the divorce hadn't happened." And added: "If only he'd been a man like Hamad." Ibtihal merely smiled. All of us would like a father like Hamad, I said to myself.

At five in the evening, the older members of the group sat in one of the coffee shops on the Champs-Élysées, while the girls went off to explore boutiques in the company of Sultan. It was customary for Hamad and his wife to drink coffee together, going from one café to the next until sunset. For them, coffee was a sacred ritual when they expressed their love for each other in the scent of coffee beans. They floated in the space of the coffee cups beneath rapturous sips, while Aunt Najwa and I looked on.

I arranged dinner at La Marina Boat Restaurant. Above the swelling of the Seine, our faces were softened in the glow of candlelight. The sound of gentle laughter mingled with the intermittent clinking of cutlery. The bustle of families formed a folk orchestra: a lone guitar, violins, rhythms from several corners and singing that connected with the meeting of glances and supplemented broken conversations. The girls were trying to get Hamad and Ibtihal to dance, but they were too shy. To everyone's amusement, Hamad improvised from where he sat by twirling his arms around her shoulders. I was captivated by the reflections in the water. I thought it odd that a river should flow in big cities such as London and Paris. It seemed to me that its presence was merely an illusion and that it no longer flowed between the towering buildings, modern shopping malls and crowds. In fact, it seemed at though the river had ceased to be an urban feature at all. I felt that it had been pushed away, ostracised like a deformed man or a beggar to live on the outskirts of the city, unlike the river in cities like Cairo and Baghdad. In those places, the river is still a divine entity; it continues to exercise its pull. It sits in the middle of the coffee shop and flows between the people. It has lost neither its humanity nor its virility. It has not yet been castrated. Every year it awaits its virgin . . . Meanwhile, candles melted, the clink of forks diminished and time was extinguished.

I love the noise of trains and the screeching traffic. For my uninitiated group the Paris train station was an adventure. They dragged their heavy cases, pushing their way through the crowds and shouting to one another to be heard above the din. They saw time flash by the window, the wind in their wake, rushing past the villages, the fields, whistling in the green – green upon green. They travelled the distance between Paris and Cannes with their five senses.

. . .

Cannes, with its bustling restaurants, cafes and beach resorts, swallowed us up from our first step. Our moments ticked by rapidly, they did not want to stop. After two nights of her company, we took a luxury minibus and headed off on a tour of Nice. It was as though life were an arena filled with a festival of joy. We sat in a restaurant on the main square, which was neatly paved and surrounded by elegant establishments. Its owner was from Monaco, the head chef was Greek, the manager was Algerian and the workers were African, Algerian and Moroccan. The menu was Mediterranean. In the middle of the square were parades and performances to the accompaniment of music – ranging from the trashy to the accomplished. The scene resembled a celebration. Sultan was like a child on the morning of Eid. He kept disappearing and then suddenly popping up again in the middle of the crowd, his massive head a curiosity for the camera lens. The girls couldn't stop taking photos. We calmly looked on with smiles on our faces.

A young "dude" had followed us to Nice and sat alone a couple of tables away. I knew that composure, that exaggerated air of cool. I had seen him more than once in Cannes. But who was his girlfriend? I ruled out Hinadi as she was too young. So Mona or Hind? Both were bold and beautiful. I don't know why but I felt it must be Hind who was in some way connected to this young man. Perhaps I judged this from the unruly swelling of her breasts in contrast to Mona's bashful little ones. I needed more evidence to confirm my suspicions so I continued to stare at the details of a very private femininity. I closed and opened my eyes a few times to chase their image from my imagination and zoned out to the sound of music.

The next day we set off for Monaco. We stopped briefly at the city's most important sites. In every traditional European city there is a square and church, except Monaco. In the centre of Monaco is a Casino. We sat in one of the cafés and this time I took a good look around me, searching for the watcher or the unknown lover, or the "dude". I didn't find him. At 10pm, after Hamad and Ibtihal had

Fiction from **Kuwait**

practised their ritual of love and coffee, we went to a musical performance at the Chemis Club. Hind had made the suggestion,
backed by the overwhelming support of Hinadi and Mona. Above
us, palm trees floated in a canopy of intersecting lights. Beyond, the
sky peered in through the glass and below us artificial rivers flowed
beneath a translucent floor. The place was somehow greater than
its dimensions and time didn't seem to exist there. Wild bursts of
conversation and laughter flared up in a swirling, intoxicating mo-
saic of light, and from half-lit corners lasers shone out onto the walls
of glass booths and bounced off dancing bodies. We sat down in one
of the booths and each of us ordered a juice. Music with a western
rhythm faded out and was replaced by Arabic songs. Hind, Mona,
and Hinadi went down onto the dance floor. We could barely make
them out between the raised arms of other dancers. I was convinced
the famous singer was miming to a CD. He, a young singer who had
topped the charts for several years, performed with body and voice
amid the dancing crowd, microphone in hand. The air was hot. Absentmindedly, I began to make my way towards them. I stopped
when I heard Mona shout out in the silences between the rhythms
– "He's our companion". Hind repeated it in a louder voice. Three
young Gulf Arabs looked at me reassuringly. It was a carefully
arranged date, then. The girls were enjoying the hot lights. The father had no objections so long as certain boundaries were not

View over the Seine and Pont Neuf

crossed – but just where did the boundaries begin and end?

I was expecting to see the "dude" among the three young men with Hind, but he wasn't there. It seems that in every city we leave behind a lover and we meet new ones. I retreated to the bar hiding from Hamad, the father, like a teenager. I asked for a Heineken. In situations like this you can trust sober German imagination. My soul plunged into that beloved bitterness without waiting for the white foam to dissipate. After that I knocked back a tequila and sucked a slice of lemon. Under the influence of a growing heat of intoxication, between the salt, the sourness and the alcohol I saw Mona, an explosion of pink crowned with seductive innocence. I could almost feel her soft, ragged breath on the lips of the young stranger. It was as though I had suddenly crossed the threshold of taboo. They swayed together on the dance floor. Hind's hair was thick and wavy, its colour close to red. The arms of her companion vanished into its depths. Hinadi, who I had imagined to be the shyest of the three, went even further. She rolled her apple – that's how her head appeared against his shoulder, while he stealthily passed his lips over the marble of her neck. I plunged into another glass. All the women were arousing me. I went back to our booth and sat down close to the aunt. I felt a warm shiver.

I closed the "door" . . . As usual I was stark naked. I laid belly down on the bed and she massaged the backs of my legs. Later, in a travel journal that I had begun keeping almost a month before, I jotted down some main ideas, yesterday's events, and other miscellany, crossing out and adding as I went.

By noon, we were travelling like a circus troupe along the Mediterranean coast, down winding roads amid the Alpine foothills. Monaco was a green dot behind us . . . then white . . . then as though at the bottom of a deep abyss. The blue rippled and glistened in the sunlight, sometimes azure, sometimes turquoise. I could see the road all the way to Genoa. I saw the great sailors who had traversed the seas with sails that billowed across the ages. They had returned from the ports of the south buoyed by the winds of the Cape of Good Hope, carrying spices from the Indian coast, and having beaten their rivals, the Venetians, in the hunt for mermaids. They had travelled east, to the cities of the Black Sea, to Saldae, Le Kef, and Sarai. They had loaded up their ships for crusader campaigns, bristling with weapons, knights, and provisions and sailed to Acre,

Fiction from **Kuwait**

Haifa, Ashkelon, and along the length of the Greater Syrian coast. They had struck the biggest international trade deals with kings, sultans, khans and pirates. Within reach of our senses, their ships had ploughed the waves; their salty sea air blending with the trees of the Mediterranean. In their scent we detected the deepest roots. The scattered Italian villages slept like white and blue giants beneath the shadow of the green, craggy mountains, roofed with marble and moss covered volcanic rock. The mingled echo of our excitement settled at a roadside village.

We hadn't planned to stop at the village, but we were attracted by the market set up under a vine trellis that extended in the shade of pine trees and lemon trees, resplendently green. A little distance away cherry trees stood palely, despite the clarity of the sun's rays. Rose baskets adorned with lavender, jasmine and rosemary bloomed between pots and pans overflowing with fruit packed in transparent jars. A variety of homemade cheeses, preserves, and olive oils were displayed on a small table. On another table were handicrafts: table-cloths, spring sweaters, bracelets, and souvenirs carefully laid out in front of their sellers, the elderly ladies of the village. They reminded me of an old photograph in which a plump, ruddy peasant woman stands in a field before some trees. She is dressed in a white blouse and blue skirt. Her cheeks are freckled and her eyes are creased in a smile.

In the middle of the market's longest table were two glass jugs filled with a red wine punch. The old lady picked up a ladle from behind one of them and gestured with a quick shake. I answered "Si". She smiled exactly like the photo, except her colours were fresh and vibrant. From the silver ladle, which had a handle as long as her forearm, she poured the wine into a glass. I drank and felt the stiff mountain air suddenly slacken beneath the table. It gently shook the white tablecloths and rustled around the rose baskets and the souvenir cups before rising to the treetops of the soul. It stirred the old branches and the leaves fell with their stories. She smiled a "Grazie". I answered her with a nod and walked away. She did not know I had resolved to keep her image with me until my deathbed.

On our way to the great Italian shopping cities, Sultan developed a writhing desire to see AC Milan play, to sit in the home stadium of one of his favourite Italian teams. We would have had to cover hundreds of extra miles going north in order to make his wish come true and everyone was opposed to the idea. The "troupe" was enjoying its journey along the Mediterranean coast, passing through the amusement parks and the villages of red wine. It was reinvigorated by carefree nights spent in the hotels of a countryside verdant with the renewed hope of morning; and by trips to big coastal towns and shopping in luxury boutiques. I shuttled back and forth between hotel and shops, carrying as many of the troupe's shopping bags as I could manage. I didn't feel like a servant, I enjoyed the pain and the spirit of humility. I tried to forget how much coming and going my service had meant; the minor inconveniences and my sufferings. The transformation to a humble servant made me happy. It kept me at arms' length from my dreams, lofty dreams that fell hard but did not hit the ground. I liked to watch the storms, to run in the rain hollering at the top of my voice. I tried to deceive, with successive transformations, my most aware and obstinate organ, which I had exhausted with the sweat of distances, and convince it of the importance of the unimportant, so that I could forget, so that I could sleep. Ibtihal bought underwear costing over 5,000 euros and a couple of things for her sister, Najwa. Hamad bought Italian shoes for 1,400 euros and Mona bought a bag for ?000 euros, while Hind bought one for ?000, and Hinadi ?000 . . . . I no longer looked closely at the numbers. Every time I saw a receipt with a number ending in three zeros, I would take a peek at the bag's contents.

Excerpts from
the author's novel
Ghuyum Tahta Watar
(Clouds beneath String),
published by Arab Scentific
Publishers, Beirut 2012

WALEED AL-RAJEEB

Three Short Stories

TRANSLATED BY JOHN PEATE

The Funeral

The coffin lurched forward on sorrowful shoulders, the ranks of the procession swelling with latecomers. The dear departed had been a government minister.

The pall-bearers got into their pace, shifting shoulders to even out the heavy burden of the coffin. Meanwhile, blessings on the deceased were bestowed by all except those who could not cope with the throng: the weak, the overweight and the indolent. A stretch of the hand towards the coffin was all that was needed to offer one's respects.

Shoes and sandals soon dusted over, as respect for the dead demanded swift burial. The pall-bearers' faces puckered and the pace slowed among those more used to – indeed skilled in – long hours of sitting in offices. A son of the deceased wiped his tears away as the congregation reached the appointed place.

"Easy . . . easy . . . down . . . down."

"Forward a little . . . forward . . . God bless you for that."

The men closed ranks, shoulder against shoulder, narrowing the gaps. Pricey shirt fabric rubbed against worn, grimy cloth, and expensive cologne mingled with the smell of sweat and garlic. The professional men among them did not dare ask to stand at the front. Moments later a sonorous voice rose up: "Allahu akbar."

All responded with crowing reverence: "Allahu akbar."

Prayers ended, the coffin was swiftly borne to its final resting place. Council workers had already dug a few graves the day before, ready for dead.

"Not a day passes without hatches or despatches" one now said to his foreman.

Two men, of some religious standing and seeking more, jumped into the hole, helping out one the deceased's sons.

A voice arose from below: "Steady now . . . steady."

"Over to that side."

"Keep going, wedge some bricks under there."

"Soil . . . a little soil here."

Everyone stood around the grave until a sudden chilly downpour from the heavens sent the bigwigs running for their cars. The children of the departed, and those mourners who remained, finished burying the dear departed, with assistance from the municipal gravediggers.

10 September 1995

The Molar

He turned seven. Deep joy as he stood – on tip-toe against the wall and drew a pencil line above his head. He compared those two momentous lines. Yes, he had turned seven.

His father said there were conditions for growing up. Turning seven meant losing your milk teeth. Losing anything nice at seven was a true loss. Why couldn't you change teeth in your sleep? His father with the newspaper; himself with the mirror, watching his tooth waggle back and forth under his finger. Don't people grow up without losing teeth? Father, with the paper, head shaking; himself and the mirror, tooth waggling left and right. Who'll pull it out? Up to you, said father.

A string stretched between tooth and door-knob; watching on. It wouldn't come out, even with a slam of the door. Maybe the time wasn't right? Father shook his head. His little fingers in his mouth; Father g on; his little hand twisting his jaw. It wouldn't come out. Maybe the time wasn't right. People don't grow up without losing their teeth, father told him sharply. It wouldn't shift on the chair. It wouldn't shift on the floor. Father watched on. It wouldn't shift with string, it wouldn't shift with a knock. Father pondered.

Evening passed and the tooth wouldn't come out. Maybe I haven't really turned seven? Father pondered, disappointment in his eyes. Father stepped in, the boy's little mouth submissive. I'll make you turn seven today. Show me this obstinate tooth. He pointed to where it was and Father examined it, realising it wasn't the right one.

31 March 1995

The Morning of an Ordinary Day

I t pains me to see defects working their way onto people's faces: an eye swelling up; impetigo around the mouth; a scab on the nose or a wart around the eyelid – that kind of thing.

But when it comes to these types of imperfections on my wife's face – now, that's more a question of fear than pity. That'll turn any day of mine into a living hell, for sure.

I caught sight of my wife's face one morning and panicked. Her left eye had swollen up. Still, I managed to stifle a smile when she civilly wished me good morning. A feeling of resentment plus a dash of joy ran through me when I looked her straight in the eye. I rushed to finish breakfast, trying to dodge the kind of vicious row we often have. I was tense, ready for the interrogation along the lines of: "Why won't you look me in the eye?"

Or, alternatively: "Why are you gawping at me?"

Luckily for me, she sat sipping coffee and reading the paper in silence. After a suitable pause, I ventured a tentative question: "Going to work today?"

The sheer scale of my indiscretion staggered even me, but before I had a chance to recant she replied: "Of course. Why would you ask?"

I tried to bury my face behind the paper and felt the thump of my heart as I said weakly: "Just asking."

"I know you were just asking. What I want to know is why, what for?"

I realised war would break out if I did not sue for peace there and then. "Just morning chit-chat, my love."

"Morning chit-chat starts with the weather, news in the papers, not something like that."

The only way out in this type of situation is to change the subject, so I said: "It's cold this morning . . . the weather, I mean."

"I won't put up with one more word of provocation from you," she said, sharply.

Her face looked ridiculous. On the one hand she talked with such seriousness and on the other has such a big, fat swollen eye. I hid my face in the paper, but couldn't hold a laugh in for long. I howled loudly, piquing her womanly wrath: "Right, then . . . you started it. I could strangle you and you'd only have yourself to blame."

I swear I didn't want a falling out – or a dent in my head, either – so I tried again for a swift truce. I lowered the paper from my face and told her, smiling: "No, no, no. I don't mean anything by it. It's just this story in the paper that made me laugh. The one about the guy who finds a monkey one morning sitting where his wife normally is and thinks she's turned into a . . ."

I couldn't finish, especially as my wife smiled, making her face even more grotesquely funny. I let out a huge belly laugh. I couldn't stop myself. She laughed too…to begin with, that is. Then her face changed again: "Have I done something wrong?"

So I said, still sniggering: "No, no, my love. I swear to God – it's just this story that's funny."

She looked at her watch and said: "I'm late . . . got to go."

"OK, love. See you later."

At work, the phone rang – a torrent of yelling at the other end.

"You knew my eye was swollen and you swore to yourself not to tell me."

"So you didn't look in the mirror yourself, then?"

"I didn't notice."

"What did you say to your workmates?" I enquired.

Down the earpiece I heard the phone slam.

Me? I couldn't stop myself shrieking with laughter.

5 March 1995

MONA AL-SHAMMARI

Black Kohl . . .
White Heart

A SHORT STORY
TRANSLATED BY SOPHIA VASALOU

She steps out of the bathroom fully dressed, looking like the sun on a hot midday, dazzling in her radiance, and strolls to her room. Like a sunflower, I put aside my soft toy in the courtyard and follow her. Her beauty bewitches me; between my mother and her there is an abyss of difference. I sit down before her, invigorated by the smell of cleanliness mixed with white musk and the special perfume that her hair exudes. My eyes career over the blackness of her soft hair. When she leaves it loose over her shoulders like a moonless night, the breeze gusting through to dry it faster, it is like a bounty from God; only the features of her face can rival its beauty. Her lips are always glossed with jujube lipstick. They're swollen like red cherries ripe for plucking. Her deep black eyes are like chestnuts; the black kohl makes them wider, and lends languor to her gaze. Her skin is the colour of milk mixed with honey. Enchanted, I say: "Tiba . . . you're really pretty." She laughs out loud until the rows of pearly white teeth show. She plants a kiss between my eyes: "Soon you'll grow up and you'll be even prettier." "There's no-one prettier than you in the entire universe," I retort with resolve. "You're my only solace in this place," she replies.

Things had been out of kilter between Tiba and my uncle Nasser from the very first days of their marriage. Having travelled a long way from her family home in al-Sharqiya province in Saudi Arabia, she had been shocked to discover the knight in shining armour that was lying in wait for her. Her husband was an overweight and feeble-minded simpleton who didn't talk like grown men did, who ate like a child, and slept like a brute. He was a mentally retarded man-child, ten years older than her, who would take his pocket money every day from my grandfather to buy sweets and coca cola and who loved to sit and play with us.

My grandfather, though, had warned him to keep away from me after he broke my hand, and my father had to quickly whisk me off to Mohammad Abd al-'Al al-Utaybi, the most famous bonesetter in the area, who put it in a cast for a month. After that my uncle Nasser would content himself with playing marbles with my younger brothers Saud and Dhari under the buckthorn tree in the courtyard. They would win and take all his marbles, and he would begin to shout: "You cheats, you thieves, you bastards." Fighting would break out, and gigantic as he was, he would simply stick his hand in Saud's top pocket and rip it off without a struggle, laughing as he retrieved his marbles. Saud would burst into tears and Dhari would be shouting: "You stupid big oaf, we'll never play with you again, I swear." My grandfather would come out of the sitting room and tower in the doorway, obscuring the view of my father, who was standing behind him, and his trenchant look would sweep through the place in wrath. He would nod in my uncle Nasser's direction, and without uttering a single word, my uncle would put his hand in his pocket with the utmost meekness, take out the marbles, and hand them back to Saud. He would then retreat to his room on his huge plodding feet and burst out crying just where Tiba was sitting all perfumed and enveloped in the scent of incense, which was wafting through the entire house. "This is why," she would tear at him with her words, "your father, that crafty old fox, struck the deal with my father's wife when he registered some land there in her name, fetching me up here from al-Sharqiya all on my own. Because all the girls around here know you're an imbecile. But God won't pardon my father, with all his grey hairs, for trampling on my pride and putting me under orders, 'You're not to come back even if they feed you straw for dinner'."

In the sitting-room, my father was using great caution and exercising his customary respectfulness in expressing reproach to his father, who had insisted on arranging a marriage for Nasser, with the rationale that marriage would "bring him to reason, change him for the better and make a man of him".

"I told you, nothing will do him any good," he said. "And the worst of it is that you went out and got him a good-looking and unimpeachable girl," he said, casting his dice, as he waited for his father's reaction. His father's head remained bowed. "I think the best thing to do," he pounced again, "is to send the girl back to al-Sharqiya and set her free."

"Khaled, it's your older brother you're talking about!" my grandfather yelled in my father's face. "Don't you want what's best for him?"

"It's because I want what's best for him that I'm asking that we send the toy we brought him back to where we got it from."

At that, my grandfather stood up from his seat to put an end to the onward march of blame. "Let's wait and see whether God decides to bless him with children — it might bring him to reason and change him for the better."

My father went out, choking back his laughter. "Is my father really day-dreaming to such a degree?" he says to my mother. She then eagerly shares a secret that would cause him to lose sleep if he knew. "Imagine if he knew she was still a virgin – he'd die of grief." My father twirls his moustache in some giddiness: "Don't burden your conscience by saying things that aren't true."

"I swear to God, Tiba is a virgin. She told me so herself."

One of the few times my grandfather gives Tiba permission to go to the souk, he stipulates that she take me along with her. He grants us permission to leave the house after putting in her hands a small purse that is heavy with cash. At the Marzouq souk, halfway down Badawiya Street, Tiba moves about hurriedly. From the women's stalls, she buys some material, also lipstick, incense and hair perfume, and she doesn't forget to buy me chocolate, some henna and sour milk. We load ourselves with bags, and our footsteps throw up clouds of dust as we walk the long distance from Marzouq souk to – the fish souk by the sea. Tiba hastens her pace. A sense of astonishment grabs me. She turns aside to the stalls where young boys are hanging about touting their wares, offering chickens, pigeons, birds and cats for sale. "I got birds, I got chickens," they tout, "Call it a dozen, call it six." I tug at Tiba's abaya and she looks at me through her face cover. "What are we doing here?" She walks on without replying. She comes to a halt in front of a boy selling cats. He asks her what she wants and she whispers: "A sick cat." He gives a sly laugh as if he were standing face to face with a health inspector. "Impossible," he replies, "all my cats are in blooming health." "What's your price for a healthy cat?" she asks. "A quarter dinar," he says. "Give me a sick cat on the spot and you'll have a dinar." The boy realises this is not an offer to be taken lightly. He turns around to a wooden cage just behind him and draws out a gaunt and sickly-looking cat whose white fur has turned grey; it puts up no resistance. Tiba looks it over. "It doesn't meow. It will do."

A shudder runs through me, travelling up from my feet to the ends of my hair where it begins to scatter pinpricks all over my head. "Good God!" Again I tug at her abaya. "Why sick?" "It's sick now because it's hungry," she whispers into my ear, "but when it eats the mice in my room it will get better."

"And how will we carry it when it's sick?" The boy steps in with authority: "Don't you worry. Just give me a second and I'll put it in a sack for you." True to his word, he throws the cat into the bottom of a sack and fastens it at the top. Tiba hands him the dinar and we hurry back home. On the way back, she urges me not to tell anyone else about the cat, and to keep it as a secret between us. When we're nearing the house, she asks me to go in first to make sure my grandfather won't see the sack, because he would object to having a cat in the house. I open the door wide enough to reconnoitre the scene; the courtyard is empty. I give her the "all clear" with a wink and she hastens to her room.

The mystery of the cat continued to eat away at me, but I didn't mention it to anyone. I gave my mother the henna and the perfume Tiba had bought from the women's stalls, but her mind was on the dinner she was busy cooking. My mother spends every minute of her day in the kitchen, and the smell she trails is the smell of garlic, onion and spices. She has never bothered about her appearance, being far more concerned with ensuring we always had the best food to eat. "Are you fattening us like cattle? You should take care of yourself instead," I would say to her in exasperation. "You're growing up, my darling child," she would laugh in reply. "Do you want me to be like Tiba? She's a fashionista, full of airs, the only thing she cares about is her body or her hair. And even though she's got nothing to do, she takes no responsibility, and she won't take a single step inside the kitchen."

A few months later, my uncle Nasser's health suddenly took a turn for the worse. A strange illness took hold of him, and he would cough and cough until it seemed his soul was about to leave his body. My grandfather called in the Indian doctor from the medical centre, and his diagnosis was "severe pulmonary infection and respiratory difficulty, bearing similarities to the symptoms of chronic feline anthrax".

My grandfather didn't understand the diagnosis. The doctor put my uncle on a course of treatment for two weeks, but his condition did not improve. My grandfather then summoned the local pharmacist, who wrote out a prescription for natural herbs to be taken with hot water, in addition to those to be swallowed, along with an ointment to be rubbed into his chest, but he began to cough himself blue and his body started wasting away. My father fetched the Mullah, who read him the religious incantation for exorcising evil spirits. When he was walking out of the door, he whispered to my grandfather: "Your son is sick – this is neither the evil eye nor witch-craft."

One dreary morning, the sky overcast but rainless, my mother went out with my grandfather to consult one of the religious advisers in regard to my uncle, who was slipping away from us with each passing day. Suddenly we heard Tiba screaming. I was still asleep, as was my father. The first thing we thought of was that my uncle had died. We rushed to his room. My father pushed the door open and we found Tiba with a look of terror on her face in a red see-through sleeveless dress, her black hair flowing loose over her shoulders, her gown hitched up high so that you could see her alabaster white legs. She was standing there next to the bed in her full allure, sending a radiant glow into my father's darkness, while my uncle Nasser lay deeply asleep, oblivious to everything around him. "Is there anything wrong with Nasser?" my father cried out. "Nothing at all," she said with a coquettish air, "he's sleeping soundly." "So what's wrong then?" I shouted. "Khaled," she purred at my father with a melt-in-your-mouth sweetness, "there's a giant mouse in the room, and I'm dying of fear." I was aware of my father devouring her from tip to toe with his gaze. He swallowed hard more than once in order to put out the fire that had flared within his breast. The enchantress's kohl-drawn eyes, the scent of her incense, her perfume, her white arms, had all made him weak with desire. "Where is it?" he asked her. She sat down and pointed to the ground. "It's here, under the bed." I crouched down, pulling my father with me. We saw the mouse quickly scurrying out of view, and my father intercepted it with a blow, using one of my uncle Nasser's sandals. He picked up the dead mouse by the tip of its tail and we went out. I closed the door behind me hurriedly, out of fear that my father might crawl back before her, his defences crushed.

I asked myself: where is the cat she bought so it would eat the mice in her room? I hadn't laid eyes on the cat since the day Tiba and I had bought it – in fact I had forgotten about it altogether. "Maybe it ran away," I speculated, as my thoughts dwelled anxiously on my uncle. Having arrived at that conclusion, my mind was put to rest. Then one day my grandfather came in carrying a deep bowl of hot fava broth, and asked Tiba to give it to Nasser to drink, because it would help with coughing and was good for the lungs. Tiba took the bowl from my grandfather's hands, and closed the door of

Fiction from **Kuwait**

her room in our faces. My grandfather withdrew, dragging the weight of an unbearable sorrow that sat heavily upon his frame. I remained standing by the door; a diabolical thought had seized me: to secretly watch Tiba at work. For, until recently, she had never once shut her door in my face.

I approached the window of her room and peered through the gaps in the lace curtain. My uncle Nasser was lying on the bed, fast asleep. The bowl of fava broth in hand, Tiba went up to her wooden trunk. "Will she pour the broth away without giving it to my uncle to drink?" I wondered to myself. She lifted the lid of the trunk with one hand, and there was the cat, looking even gaunter and sicker than it had done before. So it was still here.

Tiba placed the bowl of fava broth before the cat, and the cat licked it with an ulcerous tongue. It sneezed and coughed until its saliva dribbled into the bowl. When it refused to drink any more, she closed the lid of the trunk and went up to my uncle. Rousing him from his death-like slumber with a jab of her elbow, I could hear her snake-like hiss clearly: "Wake up, wake up. Drink this. Father brought you fava broth to help you get better." Tiba held the bowl in her hands as my uncle drank the cat's impurities. "Down to the last drop, down to the very last drop," Tiba hissed. He drank it up, and went back to sleep.

Translated from the author's short short story collection *Yasqutu al-Mataru, Tamutu al-Ameera* (The Rain Falls, the Princess Dies), published by Arab Scentific Publishers, Beirut 2012

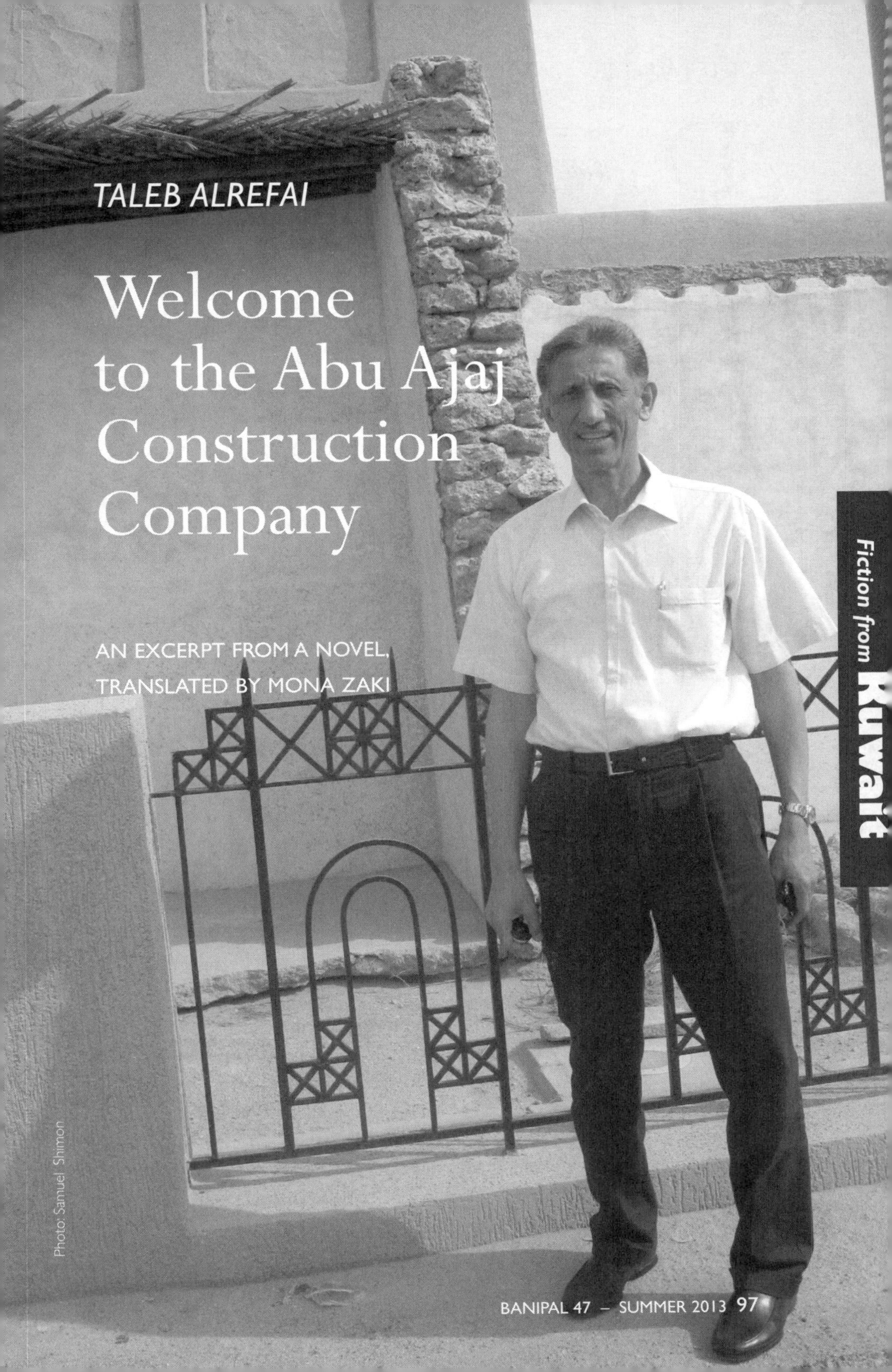

TALEB ALREFAI

Welcome to the Abu Ajaj Construction Company

AN EXCERPT FROM A NOVEL,
TRANSLATED BY MONA ZAKI

Fiction from **Kuwait**

Photo: Samuel Shimon

Dust was the first thing that greeted me in Kuwait. I arrived in the evening and the moment we stepped out of the airport, a gust of hot air slammed into my face as though it had shot out of an oven. Yellow wind. Dessouki commented: "Just your luck, my friend, dusty weather tonight."

I didn't know what to say, so I kept quiet. They walked to the car of Chief Engineer Ragai and I followed, trying to commit to memory Taleb el-Rifai's name, which I had seen on a slip of paper before we landed.

The boss, Sibai, climbed up next to Mr Ragai in the front, while Dessouki and I sat in the back. The streets were different from those in Cairo – wide streets, quiet, lit. I compared them to the confusion, overcrowding and chaos of those back home or the roads of my village. Soon a large building appeared on the left, a hotel, the Holiday Inn. Mr Sibai explained: "This is the airport road. And this is the Khitan area."

Chief Engineer Ragai drove silently on. We turned right at a large blue sign that indicated we were entering "Khitan Area". I asked myself why Khitan in particular – it was an odd plural. Dessouki explained: "Khitan is the district reserved for single men."

This surprised me since he was married, as were Mr Sibai and I. "In Kuwait there are areas restricted to families and others to single workers . . . Areas for men, hostels for workers from all nationalities, Arabs and foreigners, workers, employees, service people, men without their families, basically men without women."

"Almost!" interjected the chief engineer, as though it were a joke.

Sometimes I think I'm stupid. Never in Egypt did such a detail cross my mind, not once, like this about Kuwait. I had been obsessed with the idea of being here, it was as if I was wearing a thick black blindfold. My father had once screamed at me in a frenzy: "What genie called Kuwait has suddenly taken possession of you?!"

That first day, I woke up with the din of the plane still echoing in my head as though I was beginning a second more arduous trip. The line of a poem: "What have you done to yourself?" came to mind. Now the infatuation stage was over. I shivered and looked around me. I'm not in Egypt any more, nor in my father's house, Saneyya is not here preparing breakfast and I will not be able to call my boy, Sa'ad, to come and sit on my lap and eat with me. Here, there wasn't the smell of bread, the sounds of the village, the fields or the stream. That infatuation stage was definitely over.

Everything was different. It is a different place – the smells, the faces, the sounds, the look in the eyes, the heat and the silence. "How did I end up in this house of single men?'

Half a year of standing up to my father and I finally find myself here in Kuwait sharing a room with three men in a men's hostel. The room is rectangular and its dirty walls are a shabby yellowy white. The paint is peeling off the ceiling from which hangs a green fan. Fathi's bed is on the right with a large poster of the Egyptian actress Yousra in a bathing suit. The bed of his elder brother Sibai, our boss, is at right angles to it. A wooden plank is nailed to the wall and used as a clothes rack. My bed is on the left facing Fathi's and the pin-up actress. An old air conditioning unit blocks the only window by the door and forms part of the boss's constant gripe about how far his bed is from the cooler air.

The room had a bitter acrid odour; the revolting smell of men, the smell of exhaustion, sweat, cooking, garlic, onions, greens, un-washed chicken and meat – all spread around by the fan above. Then there was also that peculiar smell of dust. A room of beds, two to a corner.

When I walked in, I noticed the cleanliness of Fathi's sheets, duvet and pillow in contrast to Dessouki's untidy bed with its grimy lumpy pillow. There was also an ancient fridge at the end of my bed that buzzed endlessly. Fathi's closet stood at the end of his bed. On a wooden table there was a television with a video player.

I noticed a collection of short stories entitled *Abu Ajaj, May God give you Long Life!* with the name of Taleb Alrefai on the cover. Abu Ajaj is the name of the construction company that sponsored me. What is the relationship between the company I'll be working for and the stories of Taleb Alrefai? Is the fictional Abu Ajaj the same as the man who owns the company?

It was a hot and dusty day. Mr Sibai commented: "You came to Kuwait at the hottest time, Mr Hilmi. Its own people escape this summer heat!"

I stood outside the door of the room – a unit of one room. The closed doors of other rooms looked out on the same big dusty yard. I was struck by the exhausted and worn-out faces, the ceaseless drone of air conditioners and that yellow wind, which felt like a blast from an oven.

Fiction from **Kuwait**

"What have you done to yourself?" I don't remember where I read that line; it could have belonged to an Iraqi poet* who had emigrated and that line punctuated his bad luck throughout the poem.

I could not have imagined that things could be that bad. I had come from Egypt with a hundred pounds in my pocket with the idea that there was money by the bushel in Kuwait. I caught that look of blame in Dessouki's eyes the evening he had met me at the airport. We sat together that night and he asked me: "Didn't you get my letter?" I hesitated before acknowledging that I had. "Why did you rush, then?" I could not find an answer. "A genie called Kuwait has taken possession of you" was all that came to mind.

What would I say to my father and Saneyya if I returned now? That I did not find work in Kuwait? No one would believe me! I would be harangued by their astounded and disbelieving eyes. The Kuwait of petrol, money and work has no openings for a teacher! What a blockhead you are, Hilmi! This would be the chance for my father to gloat and I would be letting Saneya down, who had sold her jewellery and borrowed money from her family for this trip.

That dog of a man, Hajj Metwalli, had lied to me. He had taken one thousand five hundred dollars, the equivalent of five thousand pounds. I believed him when he said Kuwait was made of work and money. He had told me: "You'll arrive in Kuwait and see for yourself what I'm telling you."

Had it not been for Dessouki, I would have found myself sleeping in the streets. He only asked me for two hundred and twenty-five dinars and now my failure was putting him on the spot. Then, last week when Ragai was visiting Fathi he agreed to help by hiring me and said that a day's wage was four dinars.

I don't know what tomorrow would bring. I did not take to Dessouki when I first saw him in the airport with his shifty look. It brought to mind the slip of paper Taleb Alrefai had scribbled his name on.

Ragai said, as if to clarify things further: "If you work more hours, your pay will increase."

Dessouki interrupted: "Make it five dinars, Chief Engineer!"

Ragai's mind was made up: "Four dinars is the wage of a day labourer." Then, in order to press home the point that was doing Dessouki a favour, he added: "Hilmi here does not have any experience of this work, nor is he familiar with the site."

Sheikh Hassan told me as well: "Brother, don't be surprised, may God bless you, these are the rates for these companies."

On the third day after my arrival, Dessouki took me to the sponsor: the Abu Ajaj Company. This was the first time I had left the room. We walked to the bus stop in the dust and the heat. Everything was new: Khitan, the dry land with no trees, no streams or animals. The heat was overwhelming. A certain misgiving hit me – I felt as if I had made a mistake in my calculations, in my dreams and expectations. There was no money by the bushel here and no jobs lurking around every corner. In the eyes of young men I saw that needy and imploring look, their dragging feet denoting their broken spirits.

When we boarded the bus, I couldn't help noticing the burnt faces of Afghanis, Indians and Pakistanis, their skinny frames, their furtive glances, greasy hair, their peculiarly strong odours and their heavy accents. This was the first time I had seen them – I might as well have been in India, not Kuwait.

"May God aid us so we complete the transaction." The voice of Dessouki brought me out of my daydreaming, and embarrassed by my doubts I said: "*Inshallah*, God willing."

The evening I received the work visa from Hajj Metwalli he was to tell me: "The Abu Ajaj Company for Public Trade and Construction is one of the biggest construction companies in Kuwait; we've been doing business with them for years."

We got off the bus and I made an effort to keep up with Dessouki's strong stride. He was leading and I surrendered, soaking up all that was around me. We entered a big building with a glass entrance. He was walking ahead when a security guard stopped us.

The young Egyptian asked him: "Where are you going?"

"To the Abu Ajaj Company."

A voice from a gadget in the young man's hand was grabbing his attention. He barked at Dessouki: "Fourth floor", then turned back to the entrance of the building. He brought the gadget up to his mouth and started talking into it.

The lift door opened to reveal a large sign in golden lettering "The Abu Ajaj Company for Public Trade and Construction". A smiling young lady welcomed us behind a desk crowded with communications equipment.

Dessouki presented the visa and my passport and said: "Mr Hilmi here wants to have his residency stamped."

"Is this the first time?"

"Yes."

"Room number 17, Sheikh Hassan, the last room on the right."

She carried on chewing gum and pointed to a long corridor. I read the titles on the doors as we walked down: President, Director, Administrative Director, Financial Director, Conference Room, Legal Affairs, Computer Department, Real Estate Management, Head of Engineers, Technical Administration, Department of Pricing, Department of Acquisitions. We came to a large hall divided into offices. In Egypt Hajj Metawalli had commented: "One of the largest construction companies in the country."

The place was a hive of quiet activity – as if it were under the surface – sounds of employees, secretaries, typing, computers, accountants.

The office of the Head of Personnel was large, with cabinets against its walls packed with black files. The large desk in the centre was crowded with notebooks and papers and behind it sat a round-faced man in a white dishdasha with a neat black beard. He wore a small white skullcap and shawl. He received us with exaggerated formal Arabic: "*Assalamu alaikum wa rahmatullahi wa barakatuh*, May the peace, mercy, and blessings of God be with you."

Dessouki handed him the work permit and my passport.

"Please be seated. May God bless you both."

His narrow beady eyes, that small mouth in the middle of his bearded face and his sunken neck made him look as if his head were planted directly on his body. "*Bismillah al-Rahman al-Rahim*, In the name of God, the Most Gracious, the Most Merciful."

He read the visa carefully and lifting his head addressed me: "Are you Mr Hilmi?"

"Yes."

"Is this your first time in Kuwait?"

"Yes."

"May God bless you, my brother, and may your visit and work be favourable in the eyes of God."

He looked into more than one of the notebooks before him. Two other men entered the room and from the shape of their beards they looked like Afghanis. They sat as silent as statues. I wanted to ask Sheikh Hassan if it were possible to change the job description of "electrician" that was specified in the work permit.

"*Bismillah al-Rahman al-Rahim.*" He then addressed me: "*Inshallah*, my brother, we first need to get a work permit, which is issued by the Ministry of Social Affairs and Labour ."

"Are you Egyptian?"

My interruption startled him and he answered: "I am Muslim, *al-hamdulillah*, Praise to God." Then he added: "Yes, I am Egyptian."

Clearly uneasy, he gave me back my passport and visa and said: "After we get the work permit from the Ministry, we will proceed with finger-printing and then the medical check-up."

I sensed his mood changing as well as the tone of his voice, then he pushed a small paper toward me and said: "You need to pay fifty dinars at Accounts."

At first I didn't understand what he meant and I looked at Dessouki, who asked him: "Fifty dinars, why?"

"It's the company fee for signing and stamping the work permit."

The blood rushed to my head; fifty dinars was equivalent to five hundred Egyptian pounds. I objected: "But I already paid one thousand five hundred dollars in Egypt."

"Yes, my good brother, but the company has nothing to do with what you paid there."

I looked at Dessouki and caught that look of blame again. Then I said: "I want to see the man in charge of the company."

"The President is not here now, brother, and besides the fees of the company are the same for everyone." It was as if the weight of his head released words in breathless spurts out of his mouth.

"When will he be here?"

"God knows. He has responsibilities and is very busy."

His indifference annoyed me and I said: "I will wait."

He then turned to his papers and looked busy. "When will I be able to see him?" I asked a second time.

"I told you, brother, only God knows. There is no set time for him arriving here."

"I won't pay anything until I can meet the head of the company."

"Leave your phone number and we will get in touch with you."

I needed to sleep, since I would have to get up early tomorrow to begin the first day of work. How did I manage to flee the room in my father's house only to find myself in this Khitan hole? Our room back home was easier to bear; one could reach out to any friend the moment one felt locked in. I was familiar with everything there – the streets, the smell of the air, the buildings, the faces, the stories of others.

I've been a prisoner for the past three months in this damned room. Three months brooding and regretting the move amid the nauseous stale smells, the din of the air-conditioner and that picture of Yousra in her bathing suit. I lie on my back staring at the emptiness of the peeling ceiling above me, unable to find a solution out of this trap, not knowing where to go.

I lied to my father and Saneyya and told them I had already found work. In her last letter Saneyya pleaded: "My beloved husband Hilmi, please tell me about your job. Do you work in teaching or are you employed in the Construction Company?"

What work, Saneyya? What work are you talking about? Things are more complicated here than you think. I've never felt more lost than I feel right now: no family, no work, no money.

Fathi was still watching television. He is a "cute" guy, merciless about cleanliness and his clothes. He is tall, well-built, with a neat black moustache and bright eyes. The moment he comes back from the construction site, he goes to the bathroom to shower, then

Kuwait City. Photo by Samuel Shimon

combs his hair, puts on clean, ironed clothes and clean shoes, adds cologne and heads out again. I don't know where he goes. Dessouki tells me: "He works part time for an electrical company."

The night of my arrival I sensed he was not thrilled about my joining them. I ignored my hunch and it was only when he put the first porn video in the VCR that I found out why. The movie became our bond.

What would happen if I was to take a porn movie back for Ni'ma? We could stay up together watching it and act out the scenes.

I wished I had continued giving that girl private lessons. Her movements, and what they hinted at, scared me off getting involved. She was playful, giving me those languid looks that whispered of desire. I did not tell Dessouki the real reason, though, and just explained that the school curriculum was different here.

The next day, I was to begin work as a day labourer; I had no choice. I had believed the words of the cursed Hajj Metwalli: "Work in Kuwait is on every corner and money is for the taking, trust me!"

That evening, after our first meeting with the Abu Ajaj Company, Dessouki told me: "Don't worry, I will arrange things, I will speak to a Kuwaiti friend of mine who might be able to help us."

He tried to dispel the black cloud that was suffocating me. Throughout the ride back, I sat dazed and full of regret. How would I find the money? Fifty dinars was five hundred pounds. Distress is more bitter when one is away from one's homeland.

"Don't worry! It will be sorted out! This is Kuwait, after all."

Dessouki tried to comfort me. I suddenly remembered the collection of short stories; I had to find out what Taleb Alrefai had written about the company. According to his account Abu Ajaj began as a taxi driver. He took advantage of his status as a Kuwaiti and joined a company as a courier with a monthly salary of five hundred dinars, but instead of putting in the hours, he hired a Pakistani at fifty dinars a month. So Abu Ajaj started out as a con man, at the end of every month collecting the salaries of the many migrants who worked under his name, pocketing around one thousand five hundred dinars every month and handing out pittances to those substitute workers. His trade boomed, a trade in both labour and residency, until he became the owner of one of the biggest companies, the Abu Ajaj Company for Public Trade and Construction. After reading the story, I asked myself what the relationship was between Taleb Alrefai and

Fiction from **Kuwait**

Abu Ajaj.

And then Dessouki came up with the amount. He paid the fifty dinars to the accountant at the Abu Ajaj Company out of his own pocket. A representative of the company took me to the Ministry of Social Affairs, where the work contract and the permit were issued. When we returned to the company, Sheikh Hassan addressed me in a way I disliked: "Get your finger-printing done and your medical check-up and then come back here." As I was looking over the application his voice came again: "You can use our representative."

"That would be better," I said.

But Dessouki asked: "How much will he charge for that?"

"Ten dinars, *inshallah*, for the whole business – the finger-printing and the medical."

"Thank you," Dessouki said, refusing, and in a troubled voice turned to me: "We'd better go." Dessouki arranged for everything, and sent me to do it all with a representative from his employer's company.

I heard the voice of Fathi after he turned off the television in the dark: "Good night, Hilmi."

"Good night to you, too," I replied.

It was almost eleven thirty and I needed to sleep. I would start work the following day and I had no idea how it would go.

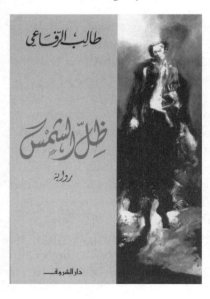

* It is a line from a well-known poem by Iraqi poet Sargon Boulus. (Ed.)

Translated from the revised second edition of the author's novel *Dhill al-Shams* (The Shadow of the Sun), published by Dar al-Shorouk, 2012 (first edition 1998).

THURAYA AL-BAQSAMI

Moscow Days

TWO CHAPTERS FROM A NOVEL,
TRANSLATED BY MAXWELL MARTIN

Deprivation Headache

Once the night lets down its dark sashes, a strange sort of activity creeps in among the residents of "Padvatelni", the freshers' dormitory. There are those who cook their dinners in the communal kitchen, and others who chat in one of the rooms. If they are Arab students, talk of politics is heated and the session ends with verbal clashes that might turn into a scuffle, though one that would be easily dissipated by the next day.

Just as the worries of exile disappear into the bottoms of tea cups for those whose sessions go no further than selling and buying words so, too, do the desires of those who seek to forget the arena of desolation in which they have gathered disappear into the bottoms of vodka glasses.

Music comes from one of the rooms, and with it, the sound of dancers' feet. A door opens and a man steps out in his pyjamas, shrieking in protest: "It's almost midnight and I can't get to sleep because of your constant commotion. If you don't stop this clatter you call music, I swear I'm going to complain about you to the de-journi."

Usually, such issues never reach the superintendent's desk. The dancers treat the disgruntled student with courtesy and allay his anger with a drink and a bit of salami napping on a slice of cheese, and by offering him the golden opportunity to dance with a girl and start up a new relationship.

On one of those nights, she felt a loneliness clothed in weariness. Her spirit wavered and she longed for a friend, especially since her husband, Khaled, had gone to a special meeting of Arab students held in the People's Friendship University. As her grandmother had told her: "A spirit searches for spirits."

She yearned to be among a group of girls, to make light-hearted jokes as she pleased, and ignore warnings to go to bed. It could lift her spirits, whose movement rather resembled that of a dilapidated lift jammed with people.

The Arab Girls' Room, as it was called, was at the end of the hallway across from the women's bathrooms.

Among the lodgers there was Sana, a Kurdish girl in her twenties who took great pride in her origin. Her hair was a reddish colour and her eyes were the green of the Sulaymaniyah hills. Her skin was as white as a snowflake. She received her scholarship after joining the Iraqi Communist Party.

Her roommate, Hanan, was Palestinian and not yet twenty years old. Her body lacked grace, while her backside was broad and powerful and reflected her voracious love of food. But her face, which was round and shaped like a Haifa orange, was alive with cheer and there was a resoluteness in her eyes and the glitter of an unusual intelligence. Her scholarship came from the Israeli Communist Party, Rakah.

She was relaxed when she spoke about her situation, showing no sign of any discomfort: "An Israeli party, a Somali party, a Satanic party, it doesn't matter. All I hope for is a white coat and a stethoscope hanging around my neck. The Palestinian organizations and parties have proved incapable even of covering the cost of my high school in the refugee camp where I grew up. I'm prepared to kiss Lenin's beard if it will get me a good education and a future in the sciences that frees me from chasing around the dust that my mother's skirt kicks up while she's sweeping the paths in the camp."

As for Lena, she was a constant visitor to the Arab Girls' Room. Lena was there every time she visited.

Laila's face was enveloped in a sad silence and she rarely spoke, enjoying the chatting of others. When she met Lena she asked her: "Palestinian?"

"No, I'm Jordanian."

"Same thing."

"There's a big difference. The government sent me as part of a cultural exchange programme. I don't support any leftist party and I promised them I would stay strong in the face of all the Marxist and Leninist theories I would be subjected to."

Everyone agreed that Lena was a tiresome girl. Maybe she suffered some kind of inferiority complex because she was unattractive. She was squat, very short, snub-nosed and her eyes were narrow and close together.

That night, she expected to see Lena in the room and was surprised to find her with her head on Hanan's chest and her body shaking from a storm of weeping. She was wailing as though she were at a funeral. She sobbed: "I'm a virgin and it will be a cold day in hell before that changes, all because of some whore who doesn't respect my humanity!"

Hanan took Lena in a motherly embrace, despite the fact that their age difference could be counted on one hand. The prison of exile, which extended to the four floors of the building, had imposed on the students the need for such support.

"Calm down, Lena, I'll file a complaint with Miss Masha. What's happening is the pinnacle of deviance."

Sana added: "It's a brazenness that cannot be tolerated." Her sudden appearance momentarily surprised the group, but they quickly recognized her and made room for her in the circle around Lena.

"Imagine, Laila, if we told you what had happened to Lena, your hair would go grey from disgust, especially since you're a married woman and more experienced in these matters."

Lena's face was painted with tragedy. Her tortured glances had Laila conjuring up macabre images of some terrible incident. Did someone try and rape her? The dorms were filled with vulgar men whose minds were full of all sorts of long repressed thoughts. But the story Lena told wiped away all the images that her mistaken intuition had invented.

"What happens in my room every night is revolting beyond belief. It was an unlucky day when they chose Maria, the Brazilian, to be my roommate. She is sick. A sex maniac. Imagine, she calls up her boyfriend José, who is Latin American like her, from Ecuador. She throws her modesty out the window and has sex with him, paying no attention to my presence. When they first started their relationship I would leave the room and go to the lobby as soon as they started kissing and wouldn't return until after he left. But for the last week they have been like two dogs doing it in the street. She loses all sense of what is around her and becomes obsessed with fulfilling her animal urges. It is obscenity in its purest form, especially when they start making noises that sound more like they come from cats than from people. I close my eyes to avoid seeing them, and to avoid their nakedness I cover myself with my blanket, soaking the pillow with my tears. Escape is impossible, especially if it happens after midnight. Sometimes I'm forced to sleep in the hallway.

"Maria's sex parties are never-ending, and she just blatantly ignores me the whole time. When they finish, José lets out a roaring sound worse than the sound of a tree stump being ripped out. My lack of sleep has affected my grades and my ability to absorb the language lessons."

Sana jumped up in the middle of the story.

"Are you nuts? You have a great opportunity to bring this issue to your teacher and tell her that Maria's shameless behaviour is the reason you haven't been doing so well in your studies." Sana loved to give out advice, perhaps as a result of her own dilemma of being a girl fated with bad luck. Perhaps she felt compelled to confront what others considered personal freedom. "Lena, did you not think to confront Maria to tell her that the sex they have in front of you is causing you trouble?"

"Of course I spoke up. I even told her that the sound José makes prevents me from sleeping but the bitch told me, with a sarcastic smile dancing on her lips: 'José is a virile rooster and I am a hen excited by that sound. Don't forget, that your body knows best, and I can see your sexual desires dancing in your eyes. José has a friend as virile as him who has the same colour skin and short squat body type as you. He'll make you happy and transport you to a different world and then you will stop watching us and fleeing to the hallway.'

"I was so shocked by her suggestion, which betrayed her low up-bringing. As soon as I told her I was still a virgin and that that would not change until I was in the arms of my husband she accused me of being backward. She compared me to a package sealed with red wax that was returned because of a mistake in the address!"

Since Lena did not have a confrontational personality, her friends took over the task of bringing the issue to the dorm's administration. Maria was summoned and reprimanded for her immoral behaviour.

But Maria was a fierce lioness ready to defend her den of sexual delights.

"The terms of my scholarship did not mention sex among the list of prohibited activities. Anyway, I need it as a treatment because if I don't have sex every night I get a terrible headache that prevents me from concentrating on my studies. It's not my problem my roommate is a backward Arab girl, a virgin who wears a chastity belt and who is satisfied with kissing her reflection in the mirror any time she needs to extinguish her desires."

Lena's problem was solved when the Arab girls were moved into a room large enough to fit three people.

Maria and her boyfriend José got into a fight, so she replaced him with the friend she had nominated to break the seal on the package. The stream of girls fleeing Maria's room continued unabated, all refusing to share space with the randy girl who was determined to have her sex potion every night so as to avoid having a deprivation headache in the morning.

A Man's Décor

The night that Laila spent in the Arab Girls' Room was chaotic as the girls tried to resolve Lena's dilemma, her nightly struggle with her room-mate Maria, the sex maniac who would search for pleasure anywhere she could, even in the cracks of the walls.

On her way back, she found a girl sitting on the stairs wrapped in a woollen shawl. The space around her was tense with imprisoned moans that could have shattered rocks. It was Aysha – 'A Husband's Accessory', 'A Man's Décor'. These were the nicknames the other

Arab girls had given her. Aysha was a woman whose personality had been wiped out, trodden upon as she was by her husband. She was at the Institute of Professional Studies and was specialising in nutrition.

Her husband was controlling and militaristic. He had joined a group of leftist Yemeni students who received scholarships from the Soviet government and who enjoyed generous support from their own government.

Aysha seemed like a bird with a broken wing, her face painted with sadness. Her eyes were puckered as a result of constant crying. Her lot in terms of beauty was modest, but when she smiled something lit up her face as though a winter sun, oblivious in the clouds, suddenly appeared before clouds of sadness returned to cover it once more, and the magic disappeared.

Because of the invisible bonds of affection connecting the boarders of "Padvatelni", she went over to embrace Aysha and ran a tender hand over her bowed shoulder that was trembling as a result of some shock or buried sadness. She hesitated a little, then said: "Talk to me, turn your worry into a story, you can trust me, your secret is safe with me. I'm a solid rock you can break your sorrows on."

Wiping away the tears of her sadness Aysha replied: "It's my cousin. Since I was a young girl, since my hand first touched the seeds of my breasts and since the first signs of womanhood appeared in me, everyone around me on every occasion repeated that I, Aysha, was for my cousin, Ali. And I felt an intense desire to be with him, but he reciprocated with indifference and a strange coldness. I thought it was just a man's pride and sense of honour, not showing his emotions to be in keeping with tradition. We grew up and marriage plans blossomed too, but they died and were buried inside him until the news came that he had received a scholarship and begun to prepare to leave for Moscow. I knew that the bird had flown from its cage, but his mother convinced him my presence abroad by his side would be beneficial and, as I learned later, I would be a 'free maid'. I would cook and clean for him, and maybe even entertain him.

"Ever since we arrived he has become an expert in humiliating me, especially when he gets drunk and the wine starts playing with his head. He starts by insulting me and talking insolently about his relationship with other women. And he reminds me on every occa-

sion that I am, in his view, no more than a servant and that the beauty of Russian girls proves I don't belong to the race of women. He says I become uglier every time his gaze falls on their breathtaking beauty.

"He tricks the elderly concierge when he brings girls to visit us, telling her they are my friends. Then he kicks me out of the room as he metes out insults and curses, screaming in my face: 'You crow, you owl, get out of my face, let me enjoy the white flesh and the beauty you will never even get within an inch of.'

"Now I'm sitting on the steps alone while he's busy having sex with a woman he picked up from the street."

Laila responded: "You have to leave him and go back to your family. Your staying here will make you sick and your youth will waste away while he encourages your misery and dances on the corpse of your dignity."

"I told him I wanted to go back, but he threatened to tell everyone I wasn't a virgin when we married and that I was damaged goods. I don't want my family to hear this concocted story of shame that could lead to my death."

My words of consolation were mere trifles poured into a sieve. Bursting open the story only increased Aysha's sadness.

Laila returned to her room that night with the troubles of a tribe of women inside her. The places had changed, the environment was harsher, and society's ills remained, controlling them. Aysha was a victim of her heritage, which stretched back centuries; a woman who was trampled on every moment, by a man who was happy to ride the steed of his virility, to wield the sword of his manhood, and to enter into sexual battles while his servant of a wife listened to him from behind the door, shedding tears over her rights being given away so freely to another woman.

From the author's novel *Zaman al-Mizmar al-Ahmar* (The Time of the Red Reed Pipe) published by Dar al-Farasha (Kuwait) and Dar al-Farabi (Beirut) 2012

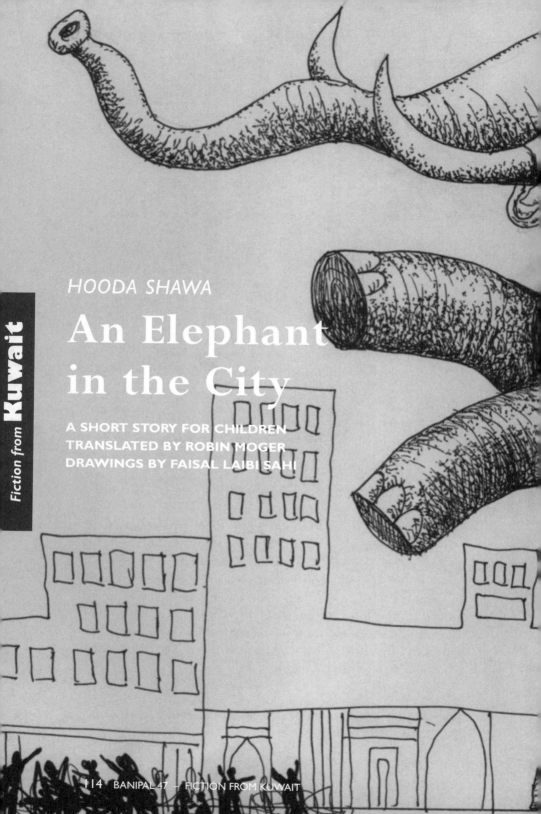

Fiction from **Kuwait**

HOODA SHAWA

An Elephant in the City

**A SHORT STORY FOR CHILDREN
TRANSLATED BY ROBIN MOGER
DRAWINGS BY FAISAL LAIBI SAHI**

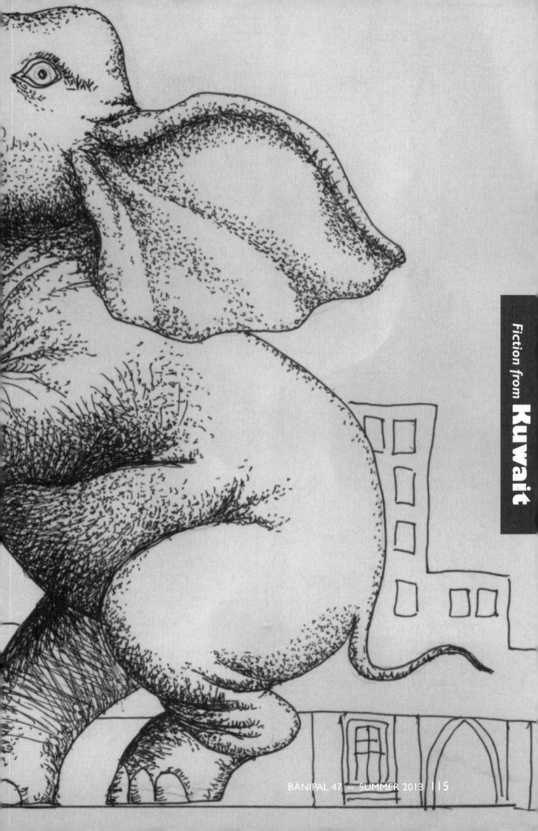

Fiction from **Kuwait**

As the city's inhabitants were waking up one morning the elephant Malek made up his mind to take the plunge.

He'd grown weary of the narrow confines of his pen.

He was fed up with the humdrum company of his wife Dalal.

He had dreamt of a new life beyond the walls of the zoo.

With a single blow of his long trunk, he smashed the flimsy wooden panels of the enclosure walls and, knowing full well what he was doing, he left the locked cage, climbed daintily over the wall and made for the zoo's main gate.

Not one zookeeper, not a single solitary employee, noticed the grey elephant's escape, for day had not yet broken and Malek, despite his massive bulk, despite his barrel body and labouring, uneven stride, was a pachyderm most calm and composed.

Through the zoo's open gates went Malek, off on a tour of the city.

The sun rose, the streets filled and on the highway, lorries, cars and vans stacked up unmoving. With the greatest of ease, supremely supple, Malek wound his way between the vehicles. Children on

their way to school stretched their heads out of car windows. A boy called out to his brothers and to his mother behind the wheel, as he rubbed sleep from his eyes: . . . "Look! An elephant's walking between the cars! Look! There's a huge elephant wandering around the city!"

And his mother, passing through a junction, said: "Are you dreaming, boy? You still asleep?"

Malek continued his slow progress along the highway. He plodded past construction sites and residential blocks, soaring glass towers and stone edifices. He walked past advertising hoardings of colourful animals, and birds in side streets, past pictures of fruit and vegetables and long grass on the side of trucks. All this made him feel sad inside; all this reminded him of the jungles back home.

Hooda Shawa

Fiction from **Kuwait**

Malek went on, across a bridge that curved down over a wide tarmacked road towards Arab Peninsula Street. When he saw the sandy shoreline he quickened his pace a little, then, joyfully, stamped his round feet on the soft sand and rolled in it and sprinkled some over his grey head. And when he came to the sea, he sunk his great barrel of a body into the cold blue water, flapping his big ears like fans. He pushed his long trunk beneath the surface and jetted out a fountain of spray that flew up to the seagulls overhead.

Fishermen in their boats stopped casting their nets and stood staring in surprise.

Joggers stopped jogging and gaped in astonishment.

Young men in their cars pulled over and started snapping with their cameras.

The city bus braked and the passengers began to shout.

One young man rushed to call the cops: "There's an escaped elephant wandering through the city!"

Angry and impatient the policeman answered: "Are you aware that these stories of yours are a waste of our valuable time? Did you know that your silly games disrupt our valuable work?"

But Malek had moved on, off somewhere new.

Passing through spacious residential neighbourhoods, he ripped thick and leafy branches from trees with his powerful ivory tusks and plucked dates from the towering palms, using his trunk.

Over in another part of the city, at elephant feeding time in the zoo, the keepers were aghast to discover that Malek, the African elephant, had vanished from his cage; and Dalal refused to eat her grass and fruits and vegetables in protest and despondency at her husband Malek's departure that same day.

A posse of officials from the zoo administration, carrying ropes and nets and with an elephant wrangler in tow, set out in convoy to find the escaped elephant before darkness fell. After wandering the city's streets, they found Malek just before sunset, rambling and romping in a park by the shore, enjoying its big, brightly-coloured games, its pools and ponds and pleasant diversions. And when he saw them he swayed his trunk in joy at the familiar faces and wanted them to play with him.

The sun had set when Malek re-entered the enclosure. Dalal greeted him with the elephants' greedy burble, delighted at her companion's return.

The officials realised that they had to expand the enclosure, fill it with toys and tall green trees and make an area with soft sand and a small pool where the elephants could roll and play and bathe, just so that Malek would stay a happy, joyful elephant and never again feel fed up or bored.

HAMEADY HAMOOD

Refugee

A SHORT STORY

TRANSLATED BY WILLIAM M HUTCHINS

He was led away within sight and earshot of his wife and children, who lacked the strength to resist in any way, except to weep and to plead with the government agents to release him. His fate had come as no surprise to him; in fact, it had happened much later than he had anticipated.

In the interrogation office, the interrogator's anger and hostility were obvious. He began questioning the man in a cunning fashion, designed to elicit at least one response that would provide sufficient grounds for convicting him and throwing him into prison for a long time, while his powerful ideas, which inflamed the minds of the people and urged them to rebel, were analyzed – or he himself was analysed after rotting behind bars.

The interrogator removed his dark suit jacket and hung it in a corner of the interrogation room. Then he set about rolling up the sleeves of his shirt after unbuttoning the cuffs. Next, he turned the chair around and sat on it backwards, leaning his elbows on the back. Finally he cast a piercing look at him. These fierce stares became a laser beam in the bright light of the old lamp hanging from the ceiling in the middle of the room. Throughout all this, the detainee did not move at all, remaining still. In fact he continued to repeat defiantly the same answers and justifications. After much effort, the interrogator sensed that what he was attempting with the detainee would never lead to anything and he despaired of ever achieving any result with him.

He proceeded to leaf through the file placed on the table over and over, thinking that perhaps he would discover something that could provide him with a renewed spark of hope – but to no avail. He shoved the folder toward the detainee so hard it quickly slid to a

stop before him and then he asked sharply: "Do you agree with what's in this file?"

"I've already told you, Mr Interrogator, I agree with you only about the authenticity of my personal data," the man responded self-confidently.

"But what is recorded in the folder before you is only a portion of what you personally mentioned in essays you have published in a number of local newspapers!"

"This is a point of contention, as you haven't produced the essays in their entirety. Instead you have cherry-picked what you wanted from them and then changed and interpreted them in a way that turns me into a criminal!"

"You need to understand that we do not serve here as the archive for your writings and that what is mentioned here is subject to only one interpretation: your insolence towards the authorities and your description of them in your latest article as "quadrupeds that stumble while attempting to lead the others of the herd". This is so clear and obvious that no two people could differ about its interpretation!"

NEXT ISSUE

SECRETS OF MARRAKECH

Photo: Margaret Obank

"How did you reach this interpretation?"

"I'm the one who's asking questions here, not you. Even so, I'll respond. First of all, you entitled your article 'The State of His Excellency M, and His Flocks', and as everyone knows, His Excellency the President (may God prolong his life) has a name beginning with the letter M. Secondly, you undertook a description of the state with its flocks and the problems it is encountering, exactly as though you were describing our state and the problems we are encountering. Indeed, you went to the extreme and mentioned in meticulous detail the boundaries of the state and its neighbours. Beyond all of this, you still persist in your statement and claim that these inferences are the product of our imagination!"

"Ha, ha, ha, ha! You make me laugh with your analysis and summaries of these matters. I am a writer, and a writer as you know has an extensive imagination. You appear to have a brilliant future in this field, Mr Interrogator. So what do you think about changing your profession?"

"If you resort to ridicule one more time," the interrogator threatened furiously, "I will throw you in solitary confinement. Understand?"

"In any case, that would be easier to bear than your analysis and accusations just so as to behead me."

"Do you expect me to believe that your most recent article was just a pure concoction of your imagination!"

"It doesn't matter to me whether you believe me or not. What's important is being true to myself and the readers."

Enraged, the interrogator pounded the table with his fist before rising to throw the chair at the wall. He turned his back to the tinted glass window and his lips moved, but no sound emerged.

The next morning, the detainee was released and returned home as happy and proud as a war hero, or the leader of a revolution that had succeeded.

In front of his house, as he was embracing his wife, who was delighted by his return, he whispered to her: "Pack my bags before they pack my coffin."

To read another story by Hameady Hamood, *Curiosity*, go to http://www.banipal.co.uk/selections/85/issue-47/

Fiction from **Kuwait**

FATIMA YOUSIF AL-ALI

Return from a "Honeymoon"

A SHORT STORY

TRANSLATED BY WILLIAM M HUTCHINS

I was hyperconscious of everything that was happening when I retrieved my suitcase from the conveyor belt and left the airport. I confirmed my return flight, hopped into the first cab, and sped off. Even before hanging my clothes in the closet, I made some telephone calls. My girlfriends received these calls with all the jubilation, delight, and anticipation of fasting people who hear the iftar cannon. Within hours we were together, gazing at the lights of the city through the car windows as if we were flower arrangements in the windows of florists' shops. Everything was fresh, as if

I were seeing it for the first time: the people, faces, signboards, cinemas, and the Opera House. I observed them all with great interest as though thumbing through the pages of an old scrapbook or album whose pictures I had fixed there myself. At the same time my heart was aflutter at discovering all the things that seemed to have sprung up in response to a conjurer's spell. The friend driving the car said: "What's trendy in Cairo today is dining on ful and ta'miya at the Jahsh." The name of this restaurant — the donkey colt — shocked me, and I felt my ears sprouting upward. I expressed my disapproval: "If we eat at The Little Donkey, they'll serve us clover."

My friend replied: "Try it before you pronounce judgment." We tried it, and quite frankly the stewed broad beans at The Little Donkey were as delicious as whipped cream and anyone who ate them once would have to keep on coming back for them — just as with our delicious Gulf fish called *naqrur*. Before parting that evening we agreed on a plan for the following day.

Like the members of any democratic Arab parliament (or other spider's web), we disagreed on this plan. One woman suggested eating fish at Christo's, another proved a partisan of *fitiir mishaltit* — layers of pastry baked in a special mud oven — at Filfila Village, a third was hungry for grilled goat meat (*niifa*) at El Dahan Grill, because at least then we could visit the Mosque of Al-Hussein and savour the next life after tucking this one into our bellies, which would be then crammed full of meat. The democratic clamour gave way to a vote in favour of Alexandria's north shore. How this decision was reached in spite of the frosty cold and the likely chance of a gale, I do not know, but we went and ate fish at the Seagull Restaurant there. We were delighted by the sea spray hitting the side of the car — it seemed to wash the rust of time from our hearts. We left Alexandria before nightfall and assembled at the door of the Cairo Opera House shortly before nine, reappearing as extremely elegant ladies after hiding our jeans in the boot of the car. Fur stoles appeared, Parisian perfumes wafted through the air, and Christian Dior stockings and shoes gleamed on marble legs. We were there to enjoy "Swan Lake". Our hearts danced to the rhythm of the music and the expanse of white on the stage swept away the sorrows of the age, disclosing the white purity of the heart concealed like a pearl inside a dark oyster shell. As soon as the curtain fell for the final time, we left the era of the swans but did not ourselves part

Fiction from **Kuwait**

company. Around glasses of hot green tea – as verdant as my heart – we finished our evening with a game of cards – after which I hung on my heart's door a sign that read "Do not disturb".

My girlfriends were amazed when I told them: "Tomorrow I will dedicate myself to the one I love. Please don't criticize me." Their eyes flashed with different interpretations of my words. I explained: "I will meet the dearest person to me in all existence. Frankly, I have tried to meet him for years and haven't had the opportunity. This is my night and the dream of my life."

Khayriya said: "What a lucky guy!" Another woman said: "I'll 'out' him."

I told her: "You won't have to wait long. I'll make an announcement and reveal the secret myself." When she insisted on knowing, I told her: "Remember what Our Master Plato said – the phrase was also written on the entrance to the Temple of Delphi – 'Know yourself'. Tomorrow I will meet with myself. Please don't intrude."

Talaat Harb Square, Cairo

Photo: Samuel Shimon

I passed the next day in silence – a queen who possessed every-thing. Silence reigned – I did not speak a word, turned off the tel-evision, and hung a sign that read "Do not disturb" by the apartment doorbell. I was satisfied with only a tidbit of food, wore practically nothing, and barely moved. I did not even raise the blinds on the windows till almost sunset, when it seemed time to bid farewell to this beautiful day.

The next day, I reconnected the phone and the festival of male and female friends burst over the line again. They told me one of the clique was defending his master's thesis at Cairo University and that we needed to mount a national response that combined words with bouquets of flowers. So we went and presented the flowers. Afterwards we presented our congratulations. Between the flowers and the congratulations, the minds of the people speaking per-formed a symphony of refined thought. Then, for the first time, I understood what Jesus meant when he said that man does not live by bread alone. He must have meant that man also lives by thought, art, beauty, and the spirit's fluttering on the horizons of discovery.

Some days later, I sensed the full meaning of departure. I thought about a place and about what would occur there. I reconfirmed my booking and listened with wonder to the cruel tones of the judge's voice announcing that I was sentenced to board flight number . . . heading to . . . I checked to see I had my passport and looked at the number of the flight once more. I passed the inspection point, fear-ful they would confiscate my delight. But I was certain that the
loveliest,
 briefest,
  swiftest, and
   most beautiful
    honeymoon had ended.

Selected and translated from the author's collection
Wajhuha Watan (Her face is a country)
published by al-Sharika al-Arabiya lil-Nashr wal-Tauzi',
Kuwait 1995

Fiction from **Kuwait**

SULAIMAN AL-SHATTI

A Voice from the Dark

A SHORT STORY

TRANSLATED BY LAYLA AL-MALEH

He kicked his blanket like someone seized with sudden fear. He was just slipping into deep sleep when the entry phone bell pierced the silence of the night. Once upon a time, when he bought the bell, he made sure it had a soft and delicate ring. But there it was, shrieking, arousing every bit of his body.

His wife, pale in the face, with signs of sleep drawn all over it, reached the entry phone first, and handed him the receiver. Her voice was scared and scratchy, : "Someone is going to die!"

A current of dread seeped into his knees. He took the receiver: "Who . . . Who . . . are you? What do you want?"

A pained and wounded voice streamed from his ear into his whole body.

"Open the door, please! I'm dying. Oh . . . help . . . help!"

He was still drowsy with the sweetness of slumber that can be interrupted just as it is achieved. It was his habit, in order to summon sleep, to recall the events of the day, adding a touch of his imagination and musing over them until his eyelids became heavy and still. He had remembered the big reception hall packed with people whose mingling voices clattered and chattered. He had reminisced over an endless talk they had had on social services; and how he, in a smart move, when the debate reached its zenith, had offered the right view and wise advice . . . When all eyes were pinned on him and when he stood there taller than ever . . . when he had raised his voice to say: "We have to rebuild the bridges which this modern age has destroyed. Don't you see how Man has become a solitary soul in the midst of crowds, lonely in his own city? This feeling of lonesomeness is wearing us out. Look at our desert! There has been a boom, thanks to those great men who populated it from one end

to another, and dedicated themselves to building its glory."

He had stopped for a moment, as if to test the weight of his words on his listeners. Pleased to see a positive response, he had proceeded: "This desert was empty save for the voice of Man, who filled its space with the noblest of ideas: assisting the needy, camaraderie, generosity; even social solidarity found an undeniable place on our list. It was that spirit of an age, now in the past, that was able to develop the highest of standards and value . . . it was an age, when good will prevailed in a manner exceeding all possible imagination. All you need do now, in order to recover that spirit is to lodge your fellow man in the left corner of your chest; and then life will take a turn for the better."

He was elated by his own enthusiasm; his throat wobbled with its fervour: "Yet we have become estranged from each other. All these cars and masses of human bodies have not made us less lonely. We have become isolated individuals cut off from kith and kin. The more crowded our cities grow, the lonelier we feel. How strange it is to feel loneliness in the midst of this mass, and how urgent the need is to reconnect and go back to the instinctive in us."

He had wanted to catch his breath and pick up a thought that was crossing his mind, when somebody decided to make an intervention: "You're absolutely right. How sensible. One can add to what our colleague has just said that . . . should we consider this great human heritage, which is beginning to slip from our hands, then we . . ."

With a charming smile, he had interrupted the speaker, picking up the thread of conversation, not allowing anyone to direct the subject away from him. Adroitly, he continued: "Indeed! I cannot agree more! What you're saying is correct, yet we must not be hypnotized by the past. I do not wish to glorify the past; I only wish to modernize its values. We have to live the present and understand its logic. We have to restore humanity to Man: this way, we will become educated and cultured individuals and rebuild society together."

Smiles of admiration coming from pretty eyes and respectable organizations lingered in his mind's eye . . . Fanciful thoughts carried him away with plans for similar meetings where he would keep his audience mesmerized by what he had in store for them. There was still one little adventure that his imagination began to scheme about. He continued . . .

The entry phone bell shrieked again.

The shrieking sound pierced his ear drums, cutting through the receiver, shattering the silence.

His body seemed on the edge of collapsing with fear.

"What's wrong? Tell me! Tell me!"

"Open the door! Help! I'm going to die. Help me please!"

He did not have the guts even to press the button to open the door. He felt his knees weak, and his tongue was stiff in his mouth.

"Won't you tell me what's wrong with you?"

"I'm going to die. For Heaven's sake, help me!"

"Did anyone hit you?"

"Oh! . . . Oh! . . . I'm dying. Open the door please!"

"Again, his hand was too weak to press the open-door-button. He put the entryphone receiver back in its place. Looking at his wife he said: "Somebody is out there screaming."

He hesitatingly tried to reach for the phone: "Shall I open the door?"

With equal hesitation his wife replied: "Wait! I'm scared! Let's think what to do!"

Everything came to a complete stop save for the voice that went on moaning in pain.

His wife suggested calling the police. "It's better if we do that," she said. "What's the number?"

"Check the phone book. I can't think straight."

His wife skipped hastily through the pages. He just watched, paralyzed by his weakness, while the voice from afar still reverberated in his ears.

"There you are! Call the police!"

Time seemed to freeze. No one answered the phone. He brushed the curtain back and stared in the darkness in the direction of the door. The moaning got louder. He had to act, and immediately.

"Shall I go and see him?"

"Wait! I'll dial again. This may be a hoax or a trick. Who knows? We're pretty far from the nearest neighbour." She busied herself with dialing. Two sounds were still hanging in the air: the phone and the screams. Two eyes kept staring into the night.

The thought that this could be a set-up possessed him. What if it were a scheme to kidnap him? He had indeed expressed some radical views in the past when carried away while addressing certain packed crowds. Some insiders could have reported his bold and often forcefully put views. He remembered an incident when he made some harsh remarks even though he suspected the presence of informants in the audience. How reckless he must have been, driven by some burning desire to go beyond astuteness to spell things out. That day, he had called for the abolition of every kind of discrimination and asserted the need to respect the humanity of each and all. He realized that this could only be achieved through clear political stances that sought just and fair social solutions. He urged everyone to denounce fear and reminded them that mutual recognition and respect was a given. Co-existence was not a choice but a must. It should be nurtured and cultivated well. One needs to make sacrifices and live and die for other people, deny the self, and be clear and transparent. All this requires courage of a special kind so that we can face all the delicate problems and prove our very existence.

Undoubtedly, this call on the entryphone is no more than a trap. He recalled stories of abduction in the darkness of the night, when anonymous hands snatched people into the unknown, leaving no trace behind, no news at all. Perhaps this was being planned today when he transgressed the permissible. They do it in cold blood now and in slow motion. He needs to be vigilant.

He imagined the pain and sorrow that would befall his family on hearing the news of his abduction. He would be the talk of the town, and everyone would look for a photo of him. They would say: "Look at him! Wasn't he one hell of a tough guy?" They might discuss among themselves why he has been kidnapped and where the kidnappers have taken him. A cold shiver shot up his spine when he realized that there was usually scant information about incidents of abduction.

Angrily, his wife heaved a big sigh, complaining that no one ever answered the phone: "What kind of emergency number is this?"

The moaning voice picked up strength after some moments of sounding muffled. No, No, NO! It cannot be a ploy. He had not transgressed much in his talk; and even if he had, they would not retaliate so openly and so promptly. Was this meant to confound him? Impossible! The voice sounded genuine, hurt and in pain.

"Then why not check him out?" His wife said: "Wait, I'll put on my abaya and come with you."

He picked up the entry phone receiver one more time: "You haven't told me who you are!"

"I'm the security man, your neighbour, the guard of the next block."

"Won't you, then, tell me what happened? Did anyone hit or stab you?"

"Oh, please help me."

Someone must have surely stabbed him, finding him all alone in that huge building. Someone must have expected to find money on him. He drew a picture of him in his mind; he saw him bent double , even crawling on the ground, raising a feeble hand to reach the bell, a move that must have hurt him all the more. In the middle of his back, he imagined a knife stuck deep in the flesh with part of the handle still showing, and blood glittering in the darkness of the night. Face down, he was seized by fierce pain, the force of which propelled him to his neighbour's door.

Wrong! The criminal did not commit his factual crime for money since the guard would not have any; besides, the building was new and deserted. He must have done it for revenge. Yes, revenge. The guard comes from a country where revenge is a common affair.

He remembered the old story of a well-known guard who killed a rival with a blow of his axe. His extended family could not offer him refuge. His uncle had simply said: "You killed him unguarded. Don't force us to hand you over to them. Run for your life, they will be after you. You are now wanted and have no protection." He had seen him only a month ago, a ghastly sight. Every bit of his body had somehow drooped, including his eyelids, so he could not see any more. A pathetic sight. Later, his country struck wealthy, to a degree, and many workers went back home. Only, he could not be a part of any of it. Haunted by his old crime, he never found the courage to make the return trip; thirty years were not enough to wipe away the blood stain.

This guard outside could be like the man of that story: strong, virile, and cautious, with marks of deep wounds on his face, speaking for this personality. His eyes would betray a look of clear mischief and slyness. Maybe there was some committed crime behind him. And maybe the avengers could wait no longer, and with the help of various modern devices were able to track him, stab him and get their revenge. Or could it be that they were not sure the stab was fatal so wanted to go back and have another go at him, making sure this time the knife would take a more precise aim at the heart.

This must be it! His chasers might be in his track, lurking in the dark, waiting for the right move.

I might get hurt in this unsolicited business.

The man and his wife could not make up their minds. She was the first to suggest that they go down and check on the "poor guy". She moved and he followed. He tried to feign courage and moved a little ahead of her. The moaning voice grew louder, stronger, piercing the enveloping silence: "Oh! . . . Oh! . . . Help! Help!"

"Wake the servant up!"

"A good idea. Two are better than one."

One needs to be cautious and on the alert. One needs to handle things carefully especially when a dreadful circumstance such as this one demands it. We should not be impulsive; we should take action in our hands rather than surrender to some reckless reaction.

He walked towards the agonized voice, which seemed to come from the direction of the main gate. He thought it wiser to open the side gate and take a peep. That would give him sufficient time to retreat in case he detected anything suspicious. But, instead, he headed towards the far side of the railings, raised his head and looked through. A man was there . . . bent double, holding on to the lamp post with a hand clutching his chest. His moaning was ceaseless. The buildings were enveloped in the dead silence of night. There was no dagger in sight. So, was this part of the ploy? He moved gingerly along the fence and his voice cracked as he asked the man what was wrong with him.

A voice, invigorated by hope, answered: "Please help me! I am dying."

At the same time, the house door opened and the wife rushed out, and behind her the servant. She stretched her hand out to give support to the guard. In the far distance, loomed the outline of a man and a woman.

The husband suddenly regained his liveliness and recovered his usual energy, while the guard, finding comfort in the man's strong arms, let his full weight fall on him.

"There's a shattering pain in my chest."

The wife asked if his arm felt numb.

"I cannot breathe . . ."

"This may be a heart attack . . ."

"I will die . . . My kids will be lost . . ."

"Seek refuge in God," someone said. And, suddenly, there were many hands supporting, lifting and carrying the guard into a waiting car, which drove quickly away.

Two hours later, the man and the guard came back, both looking good. Getting out of the car, the man said to the guard: "Just take good care of yourself! There's nothing wrong with you."

With the first rays of dawn he stood firm and self-possessed, proudly addressing his wife: "It was nothing . . . just a case of allergy . . . he's allergic to fish, yet could not resist a good meal of it. There's just no accounting for human frailty."

He began to recall the incidents of the night and mull over them.

From the author's collection
Rijal min al-Raf al-Ali
(Men from the Upper Shelf),
published by Dar al-Arouba
Bookstore, Kuwait, 2004

Fiction from **Kuwait**

FAWZIYA SHUWAISH AL-SALEM

A Night of Creation and Emission

CHAPTER FROM A NOVEL,
TRANSLATED BY GHENWA HAYEK

H e turns off the room's main light and moves the spotlight so it washes the bed. He turns on the fan, and its breeze blows my hair. He twists the red scarf around my hips and fastens it at my waist. He flicks on the cassette player, and the furious playing of a gypsy flamenco guitar blares forth. He activates the flash and snaps a picture.

Action.

The loose strands of her hair, recently liberated from their prison, are dancing. They spread down her long neck and caress her cheeks and lips. They alight on her shoulder for a moment, and then pick up their dance again, free in the fan's playful breeze, which teases the strands, newly released from the confines of the implacable ribbon. The cunning hand leads the innocent light to its goal, moving it slowly, careful that it does not miss its target. The obedient beam highlights the sensuality of the body spread out on the sheets. It floods over the arrogant breasts, pours into the navel, and flickers around it, searching for a landmark and a harbour. The lighthouse points the way, guiding the beam to the source of seduction, to its goal, the portal of the tempest and inferno. The roving, hesitant light pauses anxiously at the mound for some moments. A picture is snapped.

She raises her legs to her chest, and leans back against the pillows. The red scarf falls loose between her thighs and the sheets. The light changes direction. It sneaks up carefully, deliberately and, with a sniper's speed, aims the glare of its light at her. It disguises itself, becoming a licentious snake that slips as deftly as a breeze and as smoothly as a magic trick, inserting itself between the darkness and what the scarf obscures. With a sorcerer's puff, it insinuates itself between her folded legs and the crumpled sheets, then bursts suddenly onto the dome imprisoned between her thighs. The light comes as a dazzling flash. He presses the button and the picture is snapped.

She flips over onto her stomach, diving into the folds and creases of the covers and sheets. The red scarf is half hidden under her belly, and the ends fall on her hips. In the darkness, the light reveals all. The play of light and darkness is nothing but a game, a chase of predator and prey, a romantic dialogue.

The light surfeits the darkness. The darkness totally swallows the light, which is licentious and scandalous. The darkness is possession and deep mystery and silence. The light permeates the strands of hair dancing in the breeze of the fan, turning and turning. Through the loose strands slip rays that return – bundled into a single strong beam, thirsty for a new raid.

It continues its descent over on her shoulders and down the spine, which disappears between two hillocks.

The flowing waves of light tremble with the curiosity of a glutton, knowingly and importunately. It hesitates, turns, circles, twists, slides, touches, pours, and falls on the two hills, tumbling between them. It fingers, feels, pours into the valley between them and shines. It languishes, pants, blazes, tenses and heats up. The hand scorched by its warmth snaps the picture and extinguishes the light.

When he approaches me, his stimulants have played their role and served their purpose. His senses and instincts are aflame. He comes to me with his fires and flames. His senses have been roused by my body's thunder, the trembling of his own voice, and the convulsion of the desire running amok in him. Everything in him boils, everything in him sizzles – thanks to the appetizers, the fourth bottle of wine, two glasses of Chivas Regal, two packs of Marlboros, and an expensive Havana cigar, as well as a few unidentified substances that induce euphoria without intoxication.

The waiter keeps up his trips to our suite from room service, bringing with him fresh cocktails like Le Plaisir de l'Amour, made with rum, passion fruit and a fresh gardenia. The cocktail, which is an aphrodisiac, is the tutor of pleasure and ecstasy. Its delight lies in the secret mixture; the ways in which alcohol and fruit are blended harmoniously together. It is a blend of compounds that give pleasure – a gift to the senses and their delights. He pours me my fourth and fifth drinks so I'll ascend the ladder of desire to the levels of ecstasy he creates. This maestro of seduction knows how to provoke love and its derivatives. He sparks its fire in a different way each time, in a manner that is never boring or repetitive.

He embraces me violently and crushes me in his arms, enfolding me with the rapacity of a hunter after his prey. This game is about arousal and enjoyment. The hunter knows he is the hunter, and the prey relishes being the prey, the object of the hunt. The chase is an art in itself, and fear is one of its most pleasurable stimulants. When he unfurls me, folds me up, and uses me like a feast to sate a lethal,

Fiction from Kuwait

fiery animal's desire, his bestiality makes my heart beat faster and heats up my body. He sucks at me as though extracting my spirit. He lets me go for an instant, like a cat playing with its prey, leaving me enough time to catch my breath before pouncing on me. He sinks his teeth into my flesh and ravishes my chest, shoulder, or neck, resting there for moments – still and stubborn. When he savors my flesh too long I'm struck by fear and recall a story he told me as we walked by an old folks home where the French philosopher Louis Althusser had died after killing his wife. The strange thing was that during the investigations into her murder, he did not realize he had killed her – all he remembered was embracing her and kissing her neck.

That kiss killed her; it pierced her and sucked the life out of her. I'm afraid that his kiss will be like that one and lead to my extinction, my death. When he comes near me, I feel my end is approaching. He draws near and my heart pounds with fear while my body blazes with violent desire.

Not so fast.

The remaining moments will be mine alone and will grant me my full existence. Everything will be mine following this moment in which creation is accomplished. Everything. My essence from the World of the Unknown will now take shape.

It is now time for my appearance and arrival, which could have been effectuated and could have happened sooner.

There were other potential fathers from whose loins I might have issued. I bear the difference of another, who differs from me but is part of me. I am one of the existential possibilities I could have been and that could have produced me. The first me that I was supposed to be comes from a Lebanese father, a student at the same university as my mother. He loved her with a silent love that remained mute. He did not take any initiative, but worshipped her as one does angels who are not of human flesh. He loved her and suffered from that love to the point of sickness. Stammering, he became confused when he saw her, causing him to babble and say things he did not intend to say, things he did not mean.

What mattered was prolonging the time as long as possible – to stretch the seconds – to live as long as possible in her paradise. But her heaven held no place for a man like him, even though he was the best, most suitable match for her. Her ambitious plans had no room for long, steep ladders that would leave her breathless before she reached the top. One of her priorities was for her children to belong to a nation she was unable to belong to and that they would bring her lost identity back to her.

When she refused to marry him, he wrote her a final letter which contained everything he had been unable to say to her. Everything he had kept hidden during those years of torture, he released in one gush. She burned his letters. The flames consumed them all, except for one fireproof phrase: "I love you."

His phrase settled in her heart over the years like an ember that burned her whenever she remembered him. Had she loved him and let him down – both?

After her marriage, in Paris in fact, she had met him by chance at his clinic. They stood there, shocked, unable to speak, the silence between them chattering on by itself. When she turned and took a step toward the door, he blurted out with defeated anguish: "Give me a kiss."

Then, there was the Mercedes coupé, which raced against time to reach the object of a lifelong dream, flying at top speed, because the driver (who might also have become my father) was fearless and reckless.

His young girl friend is in her first year of love, her mind transported, floating in mysterious worlds. Love in a country that battles against love, that refuses to admit its existence, that sets up obstacles against it. Love that is stolen or kidnapped has a different taste, a different flavour. It is a blend of fear, resistance, and joy. Love snatched from time, from the eyes of parents and the judgment of the tribe, love where pleasure rubs up against danger, where adrenaline is pumped to its utmost limits. She presses down on the accelerator and the Mercedes glides forward on the wings of joy. Traffic lights bring them to a stop. But their words and their joy make them forget the street and the road. All eyes are on them, watching; love is like birth and death, out in the open, exposed.

The driver in the car behind is overwhelmed by a powerful jolt of envy and he sounds his car horn, making a continuous blaring noise. The lover, engulfed in passion, and thinking the light had turned

Fiction from **Kuwait**

green, immediately accelerates and the car takes off like an arrow aimed at a target set since the beginning of time.

The arrow's destiny was to crash into every car coming from the other direction. In an instant, in just a few incandescent moments, the Mercedes coupé, with the man and the woman and their love and joy, and their anticipated meeting, became nothing but body parts – blood spattered over a worthless metal carcass.

He used to tell that story to my mother every time she was in his shop with her friend Noura, who would try on clothes while he repeated the tale of the tragic events, recorded on an unforgettable loop.

He always paused when describing the unforgettable scene. As the ambulance men dragged him away from his mangled car, his gaze was caught by a strand of his girl friend's hair and her scalp smeared on the car's roof. The pain of his narrative captivated my mother, and she listened to him patiently, with a sad empathy. The pain of loss was contagious, and infected those near it with gloom and despair.

My mother became satiated with his sadness, and he sucked her happiness and joy away. When he asked for her hand, her answer was to escape, to run away from that infernal drama and those stories. Her escape was my salvation, since her escape gave me another life. Also, I did not want to emerge out of a catastrophic tragedy, from the stories of people touched by dark and blackened fates.

Instead, I will come from this father. From this very moment. From its beauty and its perfection, from the conjoining of male and female, of yin and yang, the two halves of the whole circle. I will be created from a raging silence, from the filling of empty gaps prepared for me before my creation, before my arrival – where I lived until my birth.

A chance coincidence, never to be repeated. A haven not available to those after me, nor to those before – because I am the intersection, the path at the crossroads through which all the roads would now travel.

He couples with me. All borders and boundaries between us are erased, and I no longer know what is me and what is him, which is my arm and where my leg is. We merge passionately and deftly. We fly and soar — bodies playing out the game of the hunt. We are ground into one another; we meld into the mash of our bodies. He comes to me with all the violence of his passion, all its unruly force. He takes me by storm. He buries me with a tyrannical masculinity. He seizes all of me. I am swept up into him. As he shakes me, all my desires collapse and all my volcanoes roar.

The savage stud knows how to rock me, how to water my passions, and in the last resort how to consume me. He throws me from a cliff, then follows me down, then swoops back up in swift shudders. He gulps, he grunts, he releases a lusty howl as he enters me. He continues moving and shaking till he reaches his climactic orgasm. He ejaculates and collapses on me, biting his lip. He lies on top of me in a calm silence, not breathing, not speaking, every muscle of him silent and quiet.

I call him. I shake him. I push him off me. I pull myself from beneath him and shout, my voice shaking with fear: "Get up! Wake up! Don't go." He does not speak a word, does not move, does not breathe, and does not respond. He bites his lip and closes his eyes in a terrible, shocking silence. I scream.

Selected from the author's novel *Salalum al-Nahar* (The Ladder of Day), published by Dar al-Ain, Cairo, 2012

Fiction from **Kuwait**

BASIMA AL-ENEZI

Black Shoes on a Sidewalk

EXCERPTS FROM THE NOVEL,
TRANSLATED BY SALLY GOMAA

Charisma

The carved wooden doors were closed as soon as Dr Fayez stepped into the elegant hall. The sound of his black Tod shoes over the blue rug with its off-white circles filled the auditorium with anticipation. This part of the third building was reserved for large-scale gatherings, celebrations, board meetings, and press conferences. The temperature was always kept low.

His meeting with 100 people in leadership positions at the firm today was a rare event due to the fact that he never stayed in any one country for more than a week. A wave of his right hand preceded his broad smile as he made his way to the podium.

He had a wide arsenal of tricks in his possession in order to quickly escape the clutches of boredom. They included addressing large crowds and drawing from them thunderous applause. It was his fate to leave behind a trail of brilliance in which others tried to bask. His photo had been in all the local newspapers today. His statements were like stones thrown into still waters, casting wide ripples.

He took his hand out of the pocket of his Tom Ford suit and ran his fingers through his thick hair. His Hollywood-perfected smile revealed white, shiny teeth. His solid frame assumed a military stance. Modesty was never his best virtue. His spontaneous unrehearsed talk got underway with unique eloquence. Listening to him was like watching a performance, where wisdom jostled with hu-

mour, insight with sarcasm, and economics with politics – his favourite subject.

He was a brilliant motivational speaker, unparalleled in the way he crafted a sense of corporate identity that made the professional world beyond his own company seem insignificant. His exceptional charisma forced his opponents to respect his intelligence even when they disagreed with the way he had managed the giant company over the last five years. He was a staunch believer in shaking things up to increase productivity. His last resolution, therefore, had ruffled many feathers.

In the first half hour of the meeting, he tackled the most dreaded topic. He wanted to replace rumour with fact and put an end to speculation. He intentionally gave short, vague answers so as to leave the door open for multiple interpretations.

Afterwards, he gave details of last year's huge income, failed schemes of their competitors, and expansion plans that had earlier been deemed unreasonable. Everyone listened carefully to the magical words of this elegant 50-year-old man, a man born to lead, to deliver speeches, to shake hands with heads of states, and, more importantly, to mythologize his own existence. Dr Fayez, whose image was ever-present in the media, always seemed out of reach in real life. Like all public figures, a field of Damask roses shielded him from scrutiny.

"We will protect our shareholders' best interests when dealing with new opportunities. We will also work harder to maintain our leadership position. This cannot take place without your sincere efforts." He rarely spoke without bringing up leadership positions.

"By 2020, 50 million new jobs will have to be created in the Arab region just to keep unemployment at its current rates. We will be facing serious challenges as job opportunities decrease and we will have to make sure our employees develop the skills they need to keep them in the workplace." Surprised eyes watched him intensely, trying to decipher what he was saying about the future.

It was a well-known fact that engineers and sales people did not make good top administrators. Fayez was the only exception to this rule. He had succeeded in transforming the company from that of a local to being global by creating a distinctive brand that positively impacted the company's place in the market.

A quick glance at his Rolex indicated that it was time for his appointment with Abu Tarek. He thanked his audience and wished them greater success. Despite their anxiety, a wave of positive energy spread through the staff. They all believed in his leadership skills and knew that any establishment in the world would be lucky to have him on board even if his annual salary was no less than one million dollars.

Now the light of the huge chandelier in the centre of the high ceiling seemed to return, after being outshone by Dr Fayez. He quickly stepped towards the door before anyone, hoping for a smile or a handshake or even a nod of acknowledgement, could delay him. His own crew made sure they gradually formed a circle around him. Some members of the audience remained seated as if pondering the possibility of switching places with Dr Fayez if only for one day. Others left their seats immediately, urged on by the expectations of almost 900 employees waiting outside the auditorium. They had spent hours every day speculating about the performance tests that were now almost over.

Just before his hand reached the shiny doorknob, his personal assistant whispered in his ear that Amwag, from Human Resources, had something urgent to discuss with him.

The Kim Kardashian Perfume

She took out a small makeup case from her brand new Céline handbag, which was blue with a brown trim. She had rushed to the ladies' room to add layers of mascara and rose-coloured lip balm. Luckily, she was wearing her patent leather Louboutin pumps today and looking feminine in her new yellow Chloé dress with its brown belt. Despite being thirty, her perfect light skin made her look younger. She sprayed herself with the Kim Kardashian perfume before heading back to her office in the Human Resources Department on the second floor, leaving behind her a trail of jasmine scent.

Human Resources either opened the door to a glamorous world by offering a dream job with grave responsibilities or led to a fast exit. Welcoming new employees and easing the transition of others into new realms were part of her daily tasks. Requisitions made to her office were endless. It was her job to prove that the firm offered countless benefits while strictly following rules and regulations.

Amwag's position was delicate; she had to cut expenses while pretending she was looking after a thousand employees and providing the best working environment.

Female employees specifically envied her for her movie star appearance with her long brown hair, her graceful figure, her unusual name, and the high esteem in which the top administration held her. Determined to open closed doors and climb the ladder of success, she never paid attention to the growing gossip around her.

She had enemies lurking in every corner. Over the last five years, she had held several important positions. Every crisis made her stronger. In her hands, dust turned into gold. She stepped on many people in her way. Many others supported her ascension from middle to top rank.

This thirty-year-old single woman pursued her job like a force of nature. If she was angry, the whole place turned quiet. At the slightest provocation, her raised voice could be heard. Employees discussed her decisions even at home. She was ranked first as their object of wrath, as the target of their nefarious schemes, and, for some, she epitomized the moral decadence of the times.

She moved closer to an incense burner and let its scent waft through her long hair. She disentangled a Chanel earring with the same expediency with which she had disentangled herself from the prospect of marriage to a man who would have hindered her progress and toyed with her dreams.

There was a life-size photograph of Dr Fayez and Abu Tarek, the chief executive officer, in her office. The size of it invoked praise even from those who recognized its strangeness. She had the prime office space on the fourth floor. It used to belong to Suleiman. Out of her window, she could see the industrial district and part of the bridge near Shuwaikh Port. Pieces of paper and plastic bags were

Fiction from **Kuwait**

flying in the wind on nearby streets. The clouds were about to cry.

She took out a piece of mint gum from her new handbag. On her last trip to London where she attended a training workshop, she spent a lot of money at Chanel, Hermès, and Céline. She could not resist buying luxury handbags, especially since she came from a culture where women loved fashion and brand names.

She liked to travel to workshops from time to time because they were paid in full in addition to the bonuses she received. The firm was very generous when it came to rewarding its employees' performance. As the company's face to the world, top managers attended the best workshops at least twice a year in Europe or the United States.

Despite stiff competition, her shoes, clothes, and perfumes set her apart. In the last few years, she had taken extreme care of her appearance: her body became thinner; diamond watches adorned her wrist; and small hearts and keys made of white gold and precious stones rested on her neckline. Even her taste in perfume changed; she now wore stronger, more long-lasting ones. Soon after her second year at the job, she had replaced her old car with a white Range Rover, which she parked at a reserved spot in the second building's car park along with the rest of the top managers' cars.

In a short while, she would meet Dr Fayez. The results of the performance tests were at the final stages. Since this was one of his priorities, she had to keep him updated. Afterwards, she would call Zeid to her office to listen to his stories about the employees before she gave him the information she wanted him to report back. They would believe anything he told them at this stage, especially since they knew he had her ear. Who else could better entertain her than Zeid, a close favourite of the cream of society?

Anywhere she turned, there he was: in the newspapers, on TV, behind closed doors, and even on the road. Wherever fallen idols and false gods existed, he was to be found. The court jester was no longer a jolly fellow, summoned whenever the king felt bored or lonely, dressed in motley, performing silly tricks. Zeid was a modern-day court jester for Amwag and Abu Tarek, for the visitors to the Shuwaikh district, and for many in the past and many more to come. He fawned and flattered. He made sharp comments and funny jokes. Although he had no special skills and could not be trusted to carry out any task, he never tried too hard or seemed worried about losing his job.

He did not mind being insulted and he insulted those beneath him in turn. He was lazy and useless, but he never stopped breaking news, spreading rumours and cracking jokes. He had two catch phrases, "At your service" and "As you like".

Amwag did not like to start her day without first laughing at his jokes and receiving compliments from him and from many of the other workers. They all liked to trail the beautiful manager with the expensive bags, the movie-star looks and the intelligent remarks, vying for a small modicum of recognition.

Her job was quite different from Miranda Priestly's, played by Meryl Streep in her favourite movie "The Devil Wears Prada". There was a world of difference between the Runway fashion magazine and the Human Resources Department of this big company. Yet, she resembled Miranda Priestly in her impossible demands, her cruel attitude, her boundless love of fashion, and her expectations that others should bend over backwards for her sake. In addition, like Miranda Priestly, she believed that fashion expressed individuality.

A Slight Chance

Security guards were the welcoming presence at every entrance and exit. Whenever needed, they magically appeared. They provided the stability the firm needed.

These security men, with their Gulf features and their athletic bodies, were never employees in the true sense of the word. They played in the soccer team and won medals every season. They wore elegant black suits, ties sporting the company's colourful logo and black leather shoes. They were always clean shaven. They were young men in their twenties, perfect for their jobs. They knew all the employees, their parking spots, their office locations, their frequent guests, and sometimes even their personal traits and moods. They tirelessly watched videos from surveillance cameras mounted at every corner for the tiniest change that might disturb the peace.

They got along fine with everyone. For some, this was a second career. Many people sympathized with them because they had no clear national identity. Still, an invisible, if neutral, line divided them from everyone else. They knew each other well because they came

Fiction from **Kuwait**

from poor areas, either in Salibiya or Taima. Some were childhood friends. They had somehow managed to escape poverty and hardship and make their way to this safe haven, while the majority sank deeper in despair.

They were planted in every nook and cranny. Although they largely kept to themselves, profound sadness showed in the smiles they painted on their faces to greet visitors. They fought fires, fixed elevators, chased out intruders, reset traffic devices, and intervened in the disputes between clients and employees. Their job was to protect a place to which they had no ties, especially since they worked on an annual basis for a company that specialized in providing large corporations with professionals trained in guarding doors, directing visitors, and securing premises.

Most of them had not lived through the period between 1965 and 1985 when their fathers were treated as Kuwaitis. They were all born here. This was the place where they made their first memories. Although they could name the alleys from which their fathers and grandfathers first came, they could not be expected to develop any sense of belonging to countries in which they never set foot.

Mahdi was one of them. In the sixties his father came to Kuwait from south Iraq by public transportation to join the army. In the seventies he lived in the poor Shadadiyah settlements and married one of his distant Kuwaiti relatives. He fought in the October 1973 War as a soldier in the Kuwaiti army, which qualified him for early retirement. Because his mother was Kuwaiti, Mahdi had a slightly better chance than his Bedouin peers. Along with his siblings, he believed that his father's death, sooner or later, would catapult them into citizenship.

Mahdi, with his beautiful black hair which he styled with gel, with the dimple on his right cheek, and with his 25 years of age, had a crush on Amwag and her vision haunted him everywhere he went. The minute he saw her, he became nervous and a sweet smile made its way to his face. It distracted him from things that bothered him, such as his mother's constant nagging of his father who had turned into a burden over the years, his divorced sister's unruly children, and the tiny room he shared with his brother. He looked forward to the times she happened to walk by, carrying herself with such confidence. He knew the sound of her high heels on the white marble floor. Her brief greeting to the guards at the reception counter was enough to ruin his mood and to set him on the chase for new songs on the subject of unrequited love.

He had so many emotions bottled up in his chest. Even the ringtone of his cell phone changed according to his mood. He knew so much about her: the plate number of the Range Rover she parked in the second building's car park, the exact length of her brown hair, the attention she lavished on her nails, the way she sounded when she was happy, the small Gucci leather organizer she took with her everywhere, and the sheen of the gold Cartier bracelets on her wrist.

A jasmine fragrance always revealed her whereabouts. He could smell the Kim Kardashian perfume at the mention of her name. Bits and pieces of gossip about her reached his ears as he watched the surveillance camera videos, whether in back rooms or reception areas. He was infatuated by this assertive woman, who dictated her own terms and paid no attention to what others thought of her. Would she ever notice the adoration of her secret admirer?

Jewel

Sitting on a deep black leather sofa, twirling the beads of an amber rosary between his thin fingers, the well-known sixty-year-old CEO asked: "Those performance tests of yours are causing a lot of trouble, Fayez. Isn't there a better way?"

Fayez responded knowingly: "Please don't worry about such minor details. Your wisdom is needed to determine matters of greater importance." His eyes followed the beads in the chief's hands. Rosaries of precious stone usually caught his eyes.

"I don't like to interfere in your job. You know what you're doing. But I have been receiving phone calls from friends, shareholders, and campaign advisers. I don't want the price for your big plans to come out of my good relationships." He spoke as he looked at the Shuwaikh Port through the window a worker had just finished cleaning.

"Abu Tarek, I don't want to put you in an awkward position. Cutting our workforce from 1,000 to 700 is not an easy task. Therefore, we hired a foreign management consulting company. They will assess every individual's performance so we won't have to interfere.

Please, relax, and rest assured that everything will be fine. Speaking of which, how is Jewel? I heard she gave birth yesterday. Forgive me for not congratulating you sooner."

Whenever the conversation turned to horses, Abu Tarek's face lit up like a kid in a candy store. His passion for everything related to horses dated back to the mid-nineties. He owned a spacious ranch in Wafra. His absolute favourite was Jewel, daughter of the world-renowned Piccadilly and winner of several races. Much like her, the company run by Fayez was the jewel in the crown of the family's business empire.

Abu Tarek believed that horses were the source of as much honour and prestige as venture capital in an oil-producing country. Like his ancestors, he turned even his hobbies into money-making ventures. He had refused to sell Jewel for a million Kuwaiti dinars. Holding to the old adage that thoroughbreds became more valuable over time, he had hoped that Jewel would give birth to several foals and earn him millions.

She was born grey but turned white when she entered adulthood in her third year. Her forehead was wide, her ears small, her eyes big, her back straight, and her beautiful tail always held up high.

Whenever Jewel was sick, Abu Tarek would spend the night at the stable. He watched when her hair was groomed or her hooves clipped. He always had sugar treats to give her. Last year, she foaled a colt but he lived only two days. This caused Abu Tarek deep grief despite his superstitious belief that horses protected their owners, and that this loss warded off some evil that had been meant for him.

His great love for horses made his children jealous. On the night Jewel gave birth, he cancelled his meeting with the Secretary of Labour. He anxiously travelled all the way from the capital city to Wafra to be near her. For fear of the evil eye, he allowed no one to see her except the groom. Just two days before her delivery date, she started lactating. After patiently waiting for eleven months, Badra arrived in the middle of his worst financial crisis.

Romeo y Julieta Cigars

Dr Fayez selected a premium cigar out of his wooden humidor box. Smoking was prohibited in all offices except on the fifth floor where the exception was the rule.

All environmental health and safety measures were taken at the company, from recycling to regular mammograms and weight management. The company invested in its employees' well-being as much as it used them. It was generous towards any individual who did a good job. For this reason, the life insurance policy it offered exceeded all other companies.

He used a cigar cutter to cut the end off. His phone rang. It was his brother. He decided to ignore a call that might interfere with his enjoyment of the Romeo y Julieta cigar. His family never stopped asking him for favours. He was the successful businessman they respected and hoped to stay in touch with. He lit the cigar with a special lighter. The members of his large tribe, all 1,000 of them, annoyed him with constant demands. They all had to do with his position at the company, whether it was a job opening, a transfer, or a promotion, although the latter followed strict guidelines. Sometimes their requests were more complex in nature, such as funding small businesses, asking for special privileges, and forwarding the names of small companies that dealt with a range of items from stationary and gardening tools to office furniture and meals for employees during Ramadan.

Everyone called him to ask for a favour, to complain about something, or to score some deal. Each one thought he was entitled to a piece of the company's pie just because he was distantly related to the General Manager, regardless of how flimsy the relationship was.

"You no longer return calls. Power corrupts," they always told him with a cunning smile. But he had no time even for his own wife and children. His schedule was full; his trips quick; and his meetings nonstop. Each one of his thousand employees hoped for a chance encounter, an unexpected phone call, or even a short email. Most only ran into him in the lift when he was surrounded by his personal assistants. Otherwise, he held general meetings which were more like stage performances designed to make him look perfect by arriving at a meeting on a Harley Davidson, reciting poems he wrote in Arabic and English, telling jokes and anecdotes about his own staff, and so on.

He re-lit his cigar. His mood was already improving. He enjoyed smoking by himself because he hated the image of the nouveau riche that was associated with smoking cigars. From his window, the city

Fiction from **Kuwait**

looked peaceful despite its crowded streets and endless construction work. Soft clouds were gently parting in the sky. He remembered his college days. Studying at MIT was the turning point that launched his career. His hard work had won him the opportunity to study abroad where he met students from all cultural and economic backgrounds. They formed their own "old boys' network".

He still maintained the friendships he made in the eighties. Each member of the group had achieved great success whether financially or politically. They owed their success to each other's support. Among them were statesmen, administrators, businessmen, and public figures. Each was a high achiever in his own field.

"A man is known by the company he keeps." This was his father's favourite saying. He had had connections to very powerful people in his day. From the beginning, he had realized that Fayez was the brightest among his sons and was certain of his imminent success. He lit his cigar for the third time. Tobacco fumes permeated the air and the intense taste lingered on his tongue. Most of the cigar was gone. He wondered if it was prepared by the hands of beautiful Cuban virgins, perhaps as beautiful as Demi Moore, his favourite movie star.

Only two percent of the people in his country had PhD degrees. He was proud of striving to be among the minority in almost everything he accomplished in his life.

He always enjoyed smoking by himself. No one smoked cigars in his family. They would not have heard of Cuba's Annual Cigar Festival. This was something they considered pretentious, much like the wearing of suits and ties. They would not understand Demi Moore's appeal. He rarely smoked with his friends although they all enjoyed festive Cohiba cigars and appreciated the beauty of women like Demi Moore.

Another phone call from his secretary, reminding him that Amwag was waiting to see him.

Translated from the author's debut novel
Hitha' Aswad ala al-Raseef (Black Shoes on a Sidewalk),
published by the Department of Culture and Information
in Sharjah, 2013, after being awarded 3rd place
in the Prize for the Novel

Fiction from Kuwait

SULEIMAN AL-KHALIFI

Love at First Call

A SHORT STORY

TRANSLATED BY LAYLA AL-MALEH

Their first meeting was on the phone, their last on a road. They met after stumbling across each other's path in a quasi-absurd way. What then transpired was no more than their mutual aspiration for the unknown. True, there was more than one collision here or there; yet they both adjusted to the force of circumstance, and became enmeshed in a strange friendship.

He said: "Where have you been? Fifty-eight days and not a word? What happened?"

"Hello! Can't hear you!"

He went on: "Is your phone out of order?"

"No!"

"Were you sick?"

"Didn't I tell you I'd be busy preparing for the wedding?"

"All this time?"

"Is there anything you can do other than ask questions? Think! Imagine!"

"I'm dressed with my questions!"

"What a poetic expression!"

"I didn't notice!"

"Anyway, how are you? I miss you!"

"Me too, like a tide, it picked me up and swept me away."

A long time, longer than expected, passed before they could meet. The telephone was the door bell and the living-room and the cup of coffee and the postage stamp. Time was divided between the mouth and the ear, wherever they went: Jahra, Failaka, Alkhor, Umm el Haiman. Kaifan, abroad, everywhere.

The phone rings. He said: "Hello, good morning."

"Good morning to you, too."

"What time is it now?"

"Heavens, did you wake me just to ask that?"

Telephone conversations were what introduced them to each other. The relationship developed through tone, warmth of voice, even occasional irritation. Everything between desire and response stretched and yawned in the air. Much private feeling had to be lodged in the heart and discreetly aired in memory.

He said: "I'll be sending you a birthday gift, my love. It is a necklace made of rings."

She giggled, complimented him on his taste, and told him his gift would be closest to her heart. She got carried away: "Naughty! You're such a romantic."

He knew the giggle well. It was their only means of communication. Everything else was forbidden: taboo. No mail was allowed, no letters. A hint of a letter would have meant the guillotine. That was the only condition she imposed on their continuing relationship. Love was not to leave the phone lines; it would die in the open air.

The phone rings. He said: "Can you call me tomorrow on this number . . . ?"

"Have we forgotten what we agreed on?"

"No one will be there! It's only because the phone is not taking outgoing calls."

"OK. I'll call you on that number, but only this once."

It was time for the call. The phone rang.

"Hello! Yes, this is me, dearest one."

"I wasn't going to call. Do you want to know why I changed my mind? I just remembered something important I had to tell you. Anyone who enters your house through the main door will notice the dining-room on the right. It's wrong to cover the main wall with such a big mirror, as though it were a vulgar restaurant. I'd prefer you to cover it with rosewood panelling, to match the rest of the interior."

There was nothing in his house or hers that they did not know. Every location, every little detail, the neighbouring houses, and both surrounding gardens, were known to them: plants, this flower or that shrub, the furniture and lighting, favourite clothes, habits, features and figures, even facial details with photographic effect. Should they ever have the chance to set eyes on each other, would they immediately recognize themselves?

Armed with this information, they took particular pleasure in exchanging comments on what they knew but had never seen. A feeling of bitterness, tension or occasional vexation often marred this pleasure. It was the condition she had already dictated. All this knowledge and all this experience was only a performance, an 'echo' of some great contest, as he once described it when he was in one of his gloomy moods.

Fiction from Kuwait

Laden with visions and flashbacks, he asked: "Do you really know me? How can you? Isn't this unconventional for a Kuwaiti female?" She laughed, without a trace of derision, though with obvious concern. She came to her senses and said: "Darling, this is the only place that leaves no trace."

The phone rang. He had decided to regain his position of power. He had given his word, as a gentleman, to play the game, but where are the rules of this game written down?

He said: "Hello."

"Oh, hi! What's up? Two days and not a ring."

"Busy, as you know, piles of work. Yesterday, I had a dream or something close to a dream."

"Go ahead, what was it?"

"I dreamed that I was at the Cost Drive-in and that you were in the car just ahead of me, with a man sitting next to you wearing a keffiyeh and agal."

She giggled, rather spitefully: "Well, now you know the reason."

"I tried to wear a keffiyeh and . . ."

"It would look so odd on you!"

"But who was that guy?"

"In the dream or what you thought was a dream?"

"In reality!"

"He is my beloved – in black and white."

When they met, I mean when their voices accidentally encountered one another, hers was seductive and his was rough, manly. Her family thought she was innocent and naïve. That might have been true in her teens, but it did not apply any more, for she had become sly. Her voice grew progressively more seductive and the scales tilted in her direction. Often, she would ask him to imagine what she looked like. He would carry on with guesses until he came close to the real picture. She gave him tips, which helped him in his challenging task. But he was impatient. To the first question, he gave some ten made-up answers: I am like this . . . like that and . . . like the other.

They lied a lot, exaggerating details without deviating much from reality. As for the final "self-portrait", perfection would be an understatement.

They would call each other's bluff every now and then, and in the flurry of excitement forget details they had swopped earlier. But neither cared to tease the other when caught out.

Their first actual meeting was not planned. It meant the end of a game and their "impeccable" rules were to become inapplicable.

It was evening. Her blue Lexus, which he had only heard about but never seen, was at the garage for maintenance. Instead, she was driving a small white car and she was in blue from top to toe: her dress, accessories, make-up, jewellery, except for her gold and diamonds, and her wavy hairdo. Inside the white car, she looked like a crystal ball before the Big Bang. She drove from Kuwait University via Jamal Abdul Nasser Street all the way to the second ring road before she took the turning to Kaifan.

She drove slowly at first, as if strolling along, then went a little faster and faster, and then began to make manoeuvres as she spotted someone following her. Tense and confused, she seemed no longer capable of controlling the vehicle.

At first, she noticed a car overtaking traffic in order to stay behind her. The man at the wheel flashed his headlights, kept indicating and seemed intent on annoying her. At the end of Jamal Abdul Nasser Street, the chase became perilous, with overtaking happening from right and left and sudden swerves that would force them to the edge of the pavements. On the second ring road, overtaking was followed by sudden braking. The shrieking sound of brakes, fumes and dust hung over the road.

People stood astounded, yelling. Near Kaifan, she made a sudden turn after a scary overtaking and spat in his face. He braked, reversed, then zoomed after her, cornering her in front of a police station, where he managed to block her way. The two cars came to a standstill. She poked her head out of the window, swearing and cursing as he ran towards her, showering her with profanities. At that moment, on the cusp of an encounter after this game of brinkmanship, and as the two voices reverberated loud and clear, their eyes met and beheld for the first time the countenances of the well-known beloveds, this time in the open air.

Fiction from **Kuwait**

SAUD AL-SANOUSI

Prisoner
of Mirrors

AN EXCERPT FROM THE NOVEL,
TRANSLATED BY SOPHIA VASALOU

L et me reveal to you the way I felt about you before I even
knew you, from the moment I first heard the sound of your
voice. This was – as I have mentioned, and as you could never
remember – on the 21st of December 2002, when your warm voice
lit up the candles that had long been extinguished within me and
threw open the windows that ushered fresh air into my lungs, dis-
pelling the clouds of stifling smoke that had resided in my breast
for years. I didn't know your name; I hadn't the slightest idea what
you looked like; but there was a tone in your voice that I could have
discerned amongst a thousand other voices – just as my mother
taught me. I had never believed in love at first sight, but it seems I
had fallen in love at first sound.

At first, I managed to convince myself that what I was experienc-
ing was simply a result of the solitude and sadness I had been
plunged in ever since my mother had died and left me an orphan.
Because I couldn't understand why else I was opening the windows
and doors of my soul to you, offering you a paved access to my inner
fortress upon the merest sound of your voice. Was I in love with
your voice? I couldn't say. I felt a strange urge to listen to it. Har-
bingers of love? I was unsure, for the gates of my castle had not
swung open to any girl before you – as they did not do so again,
sadly, after you.

Fiction from **Kuwait**

Photo: Samuel Shimon

I pick up a pen and write things you will never read. I address my question to a stem, which once held a red rose that you had given me for no special reason and which still stands on my desk, inside a glass box: "Does she hate me?" The stem gives a smile as wan as itself and answers with a question: "Do you still love her?"

"No, no – I hate her."

"Would you swear to that?"

I keep silent.

"Go on, swear by her 'precious head' as you always used to."

No: I will not swear false oaths upon your head. I do not wish to be the cause of your death. I still feel regret for the crime I committed against my father – a crime you knew nothing about. All you knew was that I was the son of Dawoud Abdel Aziz, who died a martyr's death.

"How was he killed? Why?" You asked me one day to tell you more about his death; you were taking an interest in my father at the time. I told you that my father was a member of the resistance. This much you knew. He was a rare breed of man: a gentle lamb with his wife and young cub, and a fierce beast of prey with greedy hyenas. He killed many of them and he refused to flee, staying behind to defend his lair with his fellow lions. The situation was deteriorating across the country. During the daytime, he continued working at a bakery, baking bread and slipping pamphlets in between the loaves. At night, he would carry out the operations he'd been assigned. The hyenas were his only target. He killed many of them and sowed fear among their ranks. But the hyenas' cupidity – their thirst for murder and torture, for terrorising women and children, for pulling out nails and tearing out men's beards, for hanging women by their breasts from prison fans, for raping and defiling – did not let up.

At that point you interrupted me with cries of: "That's enough! That's enough please!"

But I didn't stop, I pressed on like someone trying to cover up his crime: "The idea of rape was unthinkable for the lion. He bared his teeth and flexed his claws: no hyena will lay hands on my wife. He went on killing, ripping them to shreds. And yet the hyenas went on profaning everything that was holy.

At that point he decided to take us out of Kuwait.

"Pack up your bags, Umm Abdel Aziz."

"Where are we going?"

"Saudi Arabia."

"What? And what about Kuwait?"

"I will take you out and come back to fight by my brothers' side."

That was what I had told you about my father. It pleased me to see how touched you were, to see the tears in your eyes; because I had managed to keep the truth hidden from you on that occasion.

At the time, I did not tell you that I was the one who killed martyr Dawoud Abdel Aziz, or who was the cause behind the great man's death. I ended my story with his death at the border between Kuwait and Saudi Arabia, after the vile hyenas spotted his name on a list of wanted criminals following an altercation between the lion and a number of those greedy hyenas, whose filthy drool had dampened the earth and sullied its purity. What you did not know was that one of those hyenas turned his weapon on the head of the young cub as its father kneeled before it in chains, tears of anger silently streaming from his eyes, and as its mother stood by muttering Qur'anic verses and feigning fortitude so as not to break the lion's heart.

"Are you the son of the great man?"

"Yes . . ." I replied in a whisper.

The hyenas exploded into peals of laughter, spraying drops of their foul-smelling saliva all over my small face.

"Good for you," the man with the yellow teeth went on. "Now tell me: who else is working with your father in the resistance?"

I said nothing.

"Speak up, you little shit."

"I d-d-don't know."

"How old are you, you scumbag?"

"Nine."

"Can you believe it? People your size carry weapons and go to war, and you can't even string a sentence together!"

Silence.

"Speak up, you son of a bitch."

Silence.

"Speak up, pig."

"I don't know . . . I swear by God."

"You take oaths in God's name, do you, you little rat,?"

"I swear by God, I don't know anyone." (And I did know the names of some of the greatest figures at the time.)

"Swear by your father's head, you piece of filth."

At that, I turned to look at my father, who had always admonished me, "Swear your oaths in God's name, my son, for we are His servants. Don't swear in any other name than God's. Don't make anyone else equal to God." But this time his eyes were telling me: don't swear falsely in God's name – swear by my head, my boy; swear by my head, my little cub.

"I-I swear by my father's head – "

At that moment a bullet ripped through the air and pierced my father's head – the head of the father I had sworn a false oath on, thereby causing his death.

So can I swear I hate you? Can I swear a false oath on your head, and be the cause of your death?

Even as the fires were raging within me, I seemed like a block of ice in your eyes. A strange feeling for you swept over me. I kept it to myself and didn't declare it at first, not out of a desire to keep it secret, but because there was no-one else I knew to whom I could declare what I felt. I turned my back on the written word for several days – something I had never been able to do before. My need for the written word is in every way like the human need for oxygen: I breathe words, I inhale them from books with a deep breath that fills my lungs, then I exhale them onto paper using my pen. The written word is everything to me; if I'm not reading, I'm writing, and if I'm giving my fingers rest from the labours of writing, it is only to wear my eyes out with reading. That night, however, my thoughts were in a muddle, and I couldn't focus. The written word forsook me, and instead new spoken words occupied my being. "Sorry – by mistake – sorry – by mistake – sorry – by mistake." Had your message really been a mistake? And had I also prepared the space by mistake, putting it in order and dusting it out for its new occupant?

And why not? For everything around me, after all, had happened by mistake. My mother had died on that bed in the intensive care facility – a facility that was in need of care itself, at a run-down hospital that needed another hospital to nurse it back to health. Weren't there a few too many causes of death listed in the medical report? High blood pressure led to the heart receiving an insufficient supply of blood and oxygen, which led to blockage of the coronary artery, cardiac necrosis and cessation of heartbeat. Inscribed on that yellow paper, I found a multitude of causes and illnesses that my mother had not been suffering from. Heart problems, high blood pressure, diabetes, high cholesterol – and a long litany of other ailments bearing names like arcane magic signs legible only to a select few. The truth was that my mother's death had had a single cause: it had been an accidental death. His rosary beads nearly at an end, the doctor had given the wrong diagnosis; he had picked up the piece of paper and rapidly scribbled out the names of some medicaments. Never mind whether they were suited to my mother's condition: what mattered was that they suited the amount of time he had left on his shift. He picked up the pen and wrote out the prescription using the fewest possible letters in the names, so that he could make it to his rent-free accommodation in good time and have lunch with his family, despite the fact that sick people were dying in the hospital due to his negligence.

Hadn't my father died at my feet because of a mistake I made? For, had I sworn by my small head, that is what the bullet would have pierced instead of the head of my father, exiting through his right eye, leaving him dead on the spot before he'd had the chance to roar like a triumphant lion who'd reclaimed its lair.

Weren't we driven out of Paradise as the result of a mistake made by Adam, God's peace be upon him? So, if we are living on this earth right now, it is by mistake.

May God grant me forgiveness – absolve me, Lord; absolve me, Father. I shall repeat the words you taught me as a child: "God disposes and God acts as He wills – may God grant me pardon."

Everything is over, and yet here I am, still revisiting the past and wondering: had the message really been a mistake? No, it hadn't; even if life was nothing but a collection of mistakes, your message had certainly not been one of them. For, what had made you hold on to my telephone number once my mission had been completed at the doorstep of your house, and your father had pronounced the words "Thank you, my son"? Yes, I remember, one day you told me that you had been watching me from the window of your room as I handed your mobile to your father. You were struck by my self-confidence as I exchanged words with him. What self-confidence you were referring to, given what you later learned about me, I have no idea. You told me your father was impressed with me and my manner, and more importantly, you said he was even more deeply impressed once I had told him my name: Abel Aziz Dawoud Abdel Aziz, son of the martyr, son of the great hero. And you also mentioned that your father knew a lot about my father and about his role during the occupation; which was something he had also said to me on that day. He was going on about my father's acts of valour, while I was reading the features of his face and asking myself: "The writing on this man seems familiar; I feel I've read this book before. Where have I met this man?"

I still remember how that kind-hearted man shook my hand again, with greater warmth this time, after he had asked me my name and heard my answer. A look of amazement appeared on his face. He raised his eyebrows, which were heavy with the skin of many years. He took a couple of steps back, and then knit his eyebrows, contracting them until the space between his eyes and his eyebrows disappeared. He examined my face carefully, as if he was trying to get something straight. The space between his eyes and his eyebrows lengthened, and then he repeated several times: "God's world is full of surprises, full of surprises – God preserve the great hero's son – it's a small world. Your father defended Kuwait with heroic courage and laid down his life for this land; he played a tremendous role during the occupation." He ended his words with an invocation that ripped me to bits: "I trust in God to punish whoever caused it. May God take His revenge on him!"

Was it me he had in mind? Was that invocation the cause of my present unhappiness? Was he calling upon God to take His revenge against me? I don't consider it wholly impossible, even if his invocation was a mistake, as is the way with all those mistakes that force themselves into my life.

This is what I was thinking.

I continued to burn in my fire, whose heat you didn't feel, and whose smoke you didn't breathe. I wanted to know more about the author of that message. It wasn't love, as I had imagined. It was something different, which I couldn't identify; I don't think it was curiosity, but your voice might have had something to do with it. Yes, the reason lay in your magical voice, that voice that reminds me of Orpheus and the lyre – I believe you remember it well, that story, for it was you who related this Greek myth to me.

Orpheus had a lyre, and on this lyre he would play songs of such exquisite sweetness as to make the stones melt. The moment he started strumming his lyre, the trees in the forest would begin to tremble with rapture, the animals would sway, and the birds would beat their wings in unprecedented joy. Do you remember that story? Do you remember how I used to listen to you and your stories before falling asleep?

"Hello? Abdel Aziz! Are you still with me?"

"I'm here – go on, Reem."

"You've gone to sleep!"

"No, I'm listening to you."

"What's the name of the hero of the story?"

"Orpheus. Stop it, Reem. Please go on."

"All right, then. Orpheus loved a girl called Eurydice. He loved her to the point of distraction, and she likewise. One day, while Eurydice was walking deep in the forest, she stepped on a snake. The snake bit her. Her agony did not last long, and she died."

"And what happened to Orpheus?"

"After Eurydice's death, everything changed in the forest. Orpheus began to roam through the forest playing mournful songs that threw everything around him into a state of wild grief. The animals and the birds began to follow him in silence as if they formed part of Eurydice's funeral procession. When life grew unbearable for Orpheus after the death of his beloved, he decided to visit her in the underworld, which the living are barred from. In his journey to the underworld he encountered many difficulties, which he overcame by playing on his lyre; neither the guards nor the savage beasts could prevent him from reaching his destination once they had been exposed to his heart-meltingly sweet music. He crossed the river of death and came to Hades, the god of the underworld, who at first refused to return Eurydice to him; but no sooner had that hardhearted god heard Orpheus' doleful strains that his heart grew soft and he granted his wish."

The myth had an unbelievable ending. Hades asked Orpheus to return to his world and to refrain from turning around during his journey, because Eurydice would be walking behind him on her way to the world of the living, and Orpheus was not allowed to see her in her altered form before she had emerged from the land of the dead. As he walked, he heard the sound of her footsteps behind him.

Fiction from **Kuwait**

More than once, he stopped short, feeling the urge to reassure himself that it she was really following him, but he would remember the condition and forge ahead, resisting his temptation to behold his beloved. As soon as he had crossed the gate separating the two worlds and had set foot in the land of the living, he turned to face Eurydice, but at that moment, she had not yet made it past the gate, and was still a few steps away from the land of the living. He stretched out his hand – but she disappeared, never to return.

Your voice had an effect that drew me to you without any conscious awareness on my part. It was a magic not unlike the one produced by Orpheus' lyre in the Greek myth. Talking on the phone with you one day, I told you: "Your voice is like Spring; the moment you start talking, the world goes off kilter. Winter melts into the arms of Summer, and Summer freezes in the arms of Winter. Autumn dies away between the two, and the only thing that remains is Spring. The sun shines at midnight, and puts the darkness to the sword. Flowers bloom on the icy surface of the earth, and white turns to different shades of green." This description made you happy, and it made me happy to be able to express truthfully what I felt.

The common denominator between us in the beginning was fire. The fire that had melted me down and poured me into the mould of madness at the merest sound of your voice, and the fire you would spit out angrily like a riled dragon, the fire that was burning within you – the fire of your pride, which I injured by what you perceived as my standoffish attitude and indifference.

Wednesday evening, I was sitting alone in that restaurant, looking like someone who wasn't in his right mind; book in hand, hiding the trembling of my fingers between its pages, I was searching for the girl who had no form in my imagination. My search lasted an hour and a half in that welter of voices. I was using the method for analysing and comparing voices that I had learnt from my mother, but my ears failed to pick up your spring-like voice. All I could make out was the sound of a young guy sneeringly asking his friends at the neighbouring table: "Does the fellow think he's in a public library or something?"

I feel alienated from the people around me; a vast gulf stretches between us, and there are barriers that make it difficult for me to reach out to people, to feel their presence, and to think as they do. Even though most of the people there were around my age, we had absolutely nothing in common. The guys with their trendy eye-catching clothes, the girls with full-on makeup – the whole restaurant was like a catwalk, the smell of perfume outperforming the smell of food. All the young guys cared about was to get one of the girls to look at them, and all I cared about was the sense of emptiness in the people around me.

I asked for the bill.

I went back to my little world to find the cloud awaiting me. I threw myself into its arms, unable to see anything but you, and unable to hear anything but your words. "Good evening" – yes, it was an evening full of good, one in which I laid eyes on the most beautiful face in existence after my mother's face had disappeared. "I was lucky my phone fell into the hands of an honest person" – it is rather I who kisses the hand of luck for placing you in my path. "It was a happy accident" – yes, that it was; and you were the reason why it was happy, and why I was. Then I succumbed to sleep on top of the cloud to the sound of Orpheus' strains, before I had heard his story and how things ended with Eurydice.

Sleeping on top of the cloud was a different experience: never-ending happy dreams, a constant smile on one's lips. I can't remember how many days these dreams went on for, but on the 1st of January – midnight had just struck – I remember suddenly waking up to the sound of a new text message :

From: 660XXXX
Happy New Year 2003 :)
Reem Sultan

I felt that the start of this year augured well; it was as if I had found the person who would rescue me from the grip of my loneliness. I had the sense, at the time, that hope occupies large tracts of our hearts, which we become blind to when we surrender to despair. I had not learnt from my mother that "Hope in God lives on," as she always used to say, and it was she who had almost learnt from me how to let pessimism trump anything positive.

One day during the occupation, I remember lying on one of the couches in the living room in front of the TV; my mother was playing with my hair like she used to whenever my small head rested against her thigh. She was worried about my father, who had gone out at a time when the so-called deputy interior minister, lieutenant colonel Ali Husayn Ali, had ordered a curfew between 7 pm and 6 am starting the 6th of August. All my attention was focused on my head, where my mother's fingers were sinking into my thick hair, pressing down on my scalp with their tips. Sleep began to knock on the door of my eyes. My eyelids grew heavy and my lower lip drooped, but before the thin trail of saliva had had a chance to form at the corner of my mouth, heralding my entry into the world of sleep, on the screen before me appeared a man whose voice scattered the clouds of security that I had been enjoying. His keffiyeh made it clear that he didn't come from our country; the agal holding it in place was irritably perched over his head as if it knew it was in a foreign land. His nose was pointed like a beak, and his thick brown moustache had grown over his upper lip to cover part of the lower.

"Mummy, that guy looks scary," I said to my mother.

"Hush – let me listen."

"The wheels of history will not turn back. Kuwait and Iraq form a single entity whose common destiny has been decided."

"Mummy, will Kuwait ever belong to the Kuwaitis again?"

"It will, my son, God willing. The darkness will lift and the sun will cast its warm rays on the houses and the streets as it used to."

"When? When will that happen?"

"I don't know, Abdel Aziz, but hope in God lives on."

"What does that mean?"

"You see the darkness?" She said, pointing to the window.

"Yes."

"What comes after it?"

"Day."

"So even if the sun disappears, it must always shine again."

"But even if the sun shines, it must always set again."

My mother fell silent. Unconsciously, her fingers tugged sharply at my hair. "Ouch!"

My negative way of looking at things came to me naturally. Pessimism continued to be my inseparable companion. I lost my father and my mother. I lost my childhood and my self-confidence; I lost the most beautiful days of my life, along with my hope that happy days would follow. But after I got your message, I decided to rediscover my self-confidence, and this, in fact, is what happened. I prepared myself for a new year that would be different from all the years of loneliness and pain that had gone before. I tried to coax smiles into renewing their friendship with my lips. I succeeded, and my lips acquired a new habit, having hitherto known only the habit of kissing pictures of my mother whenever I missed her. That year you became my medicine, which I became addicted to until it finally killed me. You became the air I breathed until I almost died from asphyxiation; I would hold my breath because it was part of my love for you, which I refused to expel from my innermost being. That year you came to repair the edifice of love, which was on the verge of collapsing. Ever since I was a child, my heart had been large enough for two people. During the first years of my life, my love for my parents occupied all the space in my heart. I lost my father for the good of Kuwait, and I acquired the love of Kuwait – my father's death instilled it in me – and my heart came to belong to Kuwait and to my mother. I lost my mother and Kuwait was left all alone in my heart, in need of someone who would share its solitude in the sprawling expanses of my heart; then you came along, to rebuild the pillar that my mother's death had knocked down and to bolster the edifice of love, which had stubbornly endured throughout the years, propped up by that single pillar. After reading that message, I wished I could dissolve myself into letters and recompose myself to form words of love that I could send you across the air, so they could reach your phone, and then your heart. Clambering up the ladder of courage, I wrote:

> To: Reem Sultan
> It will be a very happy year for me no doubt.
> Wishing you all the best.
> Abdel Aziz

And this is how, during the first three days of the new year, my life came to consist of a succession of incoming and outgoing messages. I would send the overflow of my storming emotions, and would receive in return lines that would render them wilder, more frenzied, more insane. From the outside, they seemed like ordinary messages; from the inside they were full of madness, concealing messages you didn't understand. Throughout this time, you were

Fiction from Kuwait

imagining that I would take the initiative to call. Yes, I was supposed to take that initiative as an oriental man, or as any man from anywhere else in the world, but I belong neither to the East nor to any other direction in this world, in fact I don't belong to this world at all, I come from a world where there is neither East nor West, I come from a world that has no sun to rise in the East and set on the opposite side, a world whose cardinal directions are different from yours, a world in which East is remembrance and West is longing, North is heartache and South is regret, a world without seasons and years, where tears fall from the sky onto an earth smouldering with anger against the times, only to evaporate and reform into clouds , and then rain tears down, again and again and again.

You had a certain boldness, or daring. You took the initiative to call, as no girl ever does. I thought you came from a different world, just like me, and that we had landed on this planet in our spaceships by accident, to meet in a space and time that do not resemble the space and time in our own worlds. That night, I sat up listening to the singer Najat al-Saghira*, whose voice imparted a bit of warmth to my cold room. The phone rang; it was you. I turned down the sound of Najat – I turned it down, I didn't turn it off.

I don't remember what the first moments were like, but I was finding it hard to take in what you were saying on account of the bewitching music that accompanied your words. Washed away by the sweet melody of your words, I couldn't understand their meaning. But I can recall the highlights of that conversation, in which we began getting to know one another. That day, I discovered you were a university student, that you relished reading old stories, particularly mythology – legends from India, Mesopotamia, Egypt, the Greek myths that I later grew to love because of you. I found out the year and day you were born. I found out you adored flowers, particularly "lilies," as you would say in your perfect English. I learned about the music you listened to, the films you liked watching, what you loved and what you hated – though I had my doubts that someone with a voice like yours could really know the meaning of hate. In that conversation, you threw the windows of your heart wide open; you talked about how unhappy you were that your parents and siblings ignored you, as the youngest of the family, and you said more than once that all you dreamt about was for the rest of your family to become aware of your existence and to show you they loved and cared about you.

When you asked me about myself, I told you I was working, and that I was twenty-five. I was married to my life as an orphan, and I lived in a big house where I occupied a single small room. I loved reading novels and poetry and watching films. You asked me what music I enjoyed listening to the most. I had no consideration for Najat that night. I said to you without a moment's thought: "The music of your voice."

The sunshine disappeared from the conversation for a few moments, and a still silent darkness descended in its place. Suddenly I heard blood-curdling shrieks coming from one of the corners of my room. They were hysterical shrieks mixed with fits of crying and frightful laughter. Loneliness was stretched out on the floor on its back. It was rising up in the air and then thudding back to the ground, and shrieking in a snake-like hiss: "Quit that – stop it – I'm burning – oh – "

The spectacle frightened me out of my wits. It was as though I was watching a demon on fire being exorcised from a human body. While this was happening, Sadness was kissing my feet and pleading with me, "Please, please stop killing my sister, I beseech you – please stop this, father."

I returned to my senses and suddenly returned to our telephone conversation. I was scared you would hear the shrieks of Loneliness and the pleas of Sadness. Before I realised what I was doing, I hung up. I turned my gaze to the corner of the room and found Loneliness staring at me angrily in a terrible silence while her breast heaved violently. Her eyes were warning me against repeating what I had just done. I was shivering in fear, until finally Sadness put its arms around me and fell asleep on my chest.

After that night, I tried to call you, but the threats of Loneliness, the pleas of Sadness, and the shackles of my diffidence made it impossible. I waited until the next day, hoping you would call back, but you didn't. I recollected that the 5th of January was your birthday, as you had mentioned in our conversation, which had taken place on the 3rd of that same month. The next day, I went to a florist to pick out the biggest and most expensive bouquet available, and I asked the owner to use exclusively the lilies you love so much. Eighteen lilies, one for every year of your life. I made a point of not including any red lilies, so as not to reveal my feelings too quickly

Fiction from Kuwait

— as if I was not already moving too quickly with everything I was doing! I took a card and wrote: "Happy birthday Reem — January 5, 2003."

I hesitated over what name to sign the card with, because I didn't know who would come to the door to receive the flowers. I thought of leaving the space for the sender blank, but it's no good receiving flowers unless one knows who has sent them; flowers become even more fragrant, beautiful, and resplendent when they bear the spirit of the sender. And so I consented to an idea that my state of mad ferment had suggested to me, and signed the card with the girl's name "Aziza".

I instructed the florist to deliver the bouquet to your house on the designated day, and I spent the day wandering through the streets and waiting for you to call, far away from my small room so that my evil daughter would not get wind of anything.

That whole day, you neither called nor messaged me. I returned to my world to be welcomed back by Loneliness, which pointed to the bed where Sadness lay as if ordering me to go to sleep next to my small son, my great sadness. I opened a book but all I could see on its pages was your image, and all I could hear as the pages turned was your whispering, until finally the message arrived, incinerating part of my loneliness.

From: Reem Sultan
Thank you Aziza :P

I feigned sadness before my Loneliness even as my heart was dancing with joy, and then I succumbed to sleep.

After that, I didn't take the initiative to send you any message that wouldn't simply be a response to a message of yours. I would often compose messages — at work, in the car, in my small world. But at the last moment, I would hesitate and change my mind. I was waiting for my phone to ring and announce the arrival of a new message the way one waits for the bell to ring in a boring class, so I could then write back to you. But after your last message of thanks, I didn't get a single message or call from you for an entire week.

There have been many times in my short life when I have had to endure the arduousness of waiting. And I don't know what exactly the connection is between my experience of waiting and the number seven in particular. We waited seven terror-stricken days for my father to be released after he refused to reveal the name of the person who had carried out the "Free Men's Operation," which had blown up one of the largest buildings the enemy had exploited for the execution of their schemes. My mother and I and the rest of the Kuwaiti people waited seven months for the land we had been despoiled of to be returned to us. After my father's death, my mother waited seven years for the Angel of Death to send her after him. I spent seven hours outside the intensive care room before my mother's doctor came out and said: "God alone is everlasting." After your eighteenth birthday, I waited for a call or message from you for seven whole days that were longer than time itself. And in the end, I would send you my wishes for your birthday and wait seven months for you to return the courtesy on my birthday.

It was as if I had gone crazy – I had gone crazy, a crazy person with eyes helplessly glued to the screen of the phone. And yet for all my longing and waiting, I was unable to send you a single message. I tried to shake myself free from the shackles of my weakness. I wrote many words, but I was too weak to press "send." I spent a lot of time thinking and trying to understand why you had grown distant. Had her parents found out about the flowers? Had this gesture killed it off for her? Surely not, surely flowers can't kill, however many thorns they might carry.

On the seventh day, I decide to kill the wait before it killed what remained of my sanity. If only it would muster the force to kill me so I could be with my mother and father again, over there in the faraway world. But waiting never kills people, it only kills their minds or leads them to paralysis; so that we then live a long life in which all we can think about is the return of what we're waiting for.

The rivers of my patience ran dry; I picked up my phone and wrote:

> To: Reem Sultan
> I've missed you, Reem

Less than a minute later, the reply came.

> From: Reem Sultan
> Well . . . why don't you call?

Fiction from **Kuwait**

And suddenly, a third hand appeared before me – I think it was the hand of Longing. It picked up the phone, dialled your number and put the receiver against my ear.

The winds of longing were blowing wildly in my heart, and the floods of desire almost swept my hesitation and shyness aside, casting them onto the banks of the river of love. I wanted to carve open a direct channel to your heart, through which I could pour in the torrent of my feelings and calm the floods and storms raging within me. I would tell you how much I had suffered during this week-long wait. I would describe how much pain your aloofness had caused me. I would talk and talk, till there was no breath left in my lungs and words had become an inexhaustible spring in my heart. Yet I found my voice stretched out on the bed beside me in a state of deep sleep the very moment your magical voice came whisperingly over: "Good evening."

After a week of longing and waiting, that phrase was sufficient to force my tears above the dam the waiting period had erected over my eyes. I was so weak. I wanted to cry, but the laws of the part of the planet we live in do not permit a man to do that, even if this man happens to come from a different world.

You were talking, you were strumming chords, you were singing – I don't know what you were doing in that phone conversation, but I was listening in silence. You told me you had stopped calling me and sending me messages because you had felt you were being a nuisance. I interrupted you at once: "Not at all! No way!" You insisted your messages were getting on my nerves, and the surest proof, you claimed, was that I had never taken the initiative to call or message you. You were right; to you I looked like someone uninvolved and lacking interest. I tried to explain that I came from a different world, but I was worried you might think I was mad. I tried to explain I was bound by shackles of diffidence, but I was worried that I would tumble down a high mountain to find your eyes looking disdainfully upon me from the summit. You made things easier when you said: "Do you know what I like about you, Abdel Aziz?"

I was silent.

"I feel you're different – you're a man who comes from a world that has nothing to do with this one."

I was pleased with your conclusion that day, as it lifted a heavy burden off my shoulders. But I didn't ask you how you had realised I was different, and whom you had compared me to in order to reach this accurate conclusion.

We talked a lot, there was hardly a topic we didn't touch on, and the most important thing that came up in that conversation was what I found out about my father. I was amazed by how many things you knew about him – you knew things about Dawoud Abdel Aziz that even I wasn't aware of. When I asked you how you knew all this when I didn't, you told me you had heard it from your father.

"Did he know my father personally?"

"Abdel Aziz! Are you serious? Haven't you seen the programme 'Heroes From My Country'?"

"Of course I have. It came out in August 1998, and I still have a copy of the episode that was about my father's activities during the occupation."

"Who was the witness to the events in that episode?"

"It was Sultan – Sultan Saif! The person who had carried out the 'Free Men's Operation' – of course – now I realise where I'd seen your father before – it was in that series. Your father was a friend of my father's, God have mercy on his soul – of course, of course, now I remember."

What a small world we live in!

It was only after that conversation that I realised why your father had shown such interest in me after I told him my name that day. Talking transported us back in time, when I was nine and you were six and we knew nothing about our fathers' heroic work. You told me the reason for my father's arrest had been his relationship with your father, Sultan Saif, who had carried out the biggest explosive strike in that period. You told me your father owed his life to my father, who refused to disclose his name despite the different forms of torture the invaders used. You also told me you that your father had told you about the time when I almost got my father arrested again when I wrote "Long live Kuwait, long live Baba Jaber" on the outside wall of our house. "Where did you find the pluck to do that," you wondered at the time, "a mere nine-year-old child?" I couldn't answer, for I too needed someone who could explain that to me. I think what I had was the courage young cubs have when their lion fathers are still alive. Yes, every ounce of courage I had died after I lost my father, after I lost my faith in justice. I couldn't accept that a brave lion could die at the hands of a cowardly hyena that gets its power by staging mob attacks; for had that hyena been alone, it would never have managed to inflict the slightest wound on the angered lion.

I had always loved my father; and I loved him more and more through you. He left the world a happy man, no doubt; he went away knowing that God Almighty had given him the means for granting life to many other people. In that conversation, you told me the story of my father and Ahlam, that girl who was almost raped by the hyenas right before the eyes of her old father and her brother Youssef, who died from a heart attack while he was tied up – he died from the wounds dealt to his honour by those filthy hyenas. You told me that Youssef was a member of the resistance and a friend of my father's. My father found out that the hungry hyenas were heading for Youssef's house in order to arrest him after forcing him to confess, using the vilest and most sordid means of psychological torture. For when they had thrown his sister to the ground in front of him and his old father, when they had stripped her of her clothes, Youssef could no longer restrain himself; his whole body went into a shudder and his hair stood on edge faced with that horrific spectacle. "I confess," he cried out, "I confess, I'm a member of the resistance, I confess to all the charges brought against me, only stop what you're doing."

"You'll be telling us everything we want to know once we've had a bit of fun with this pretty lass."

Youssef gave a final cry that shook the walls of the house and then dropped dead on the spot, his glassy eyes turned to the door through which my father entered to start shooting those vile hyenas, leaving the walls of Youssef's house and Ahlam's naked body besmirched with their foul blood. He completed his task and then rushed out of the house, but he did not escape the fire of the soldiers who were deployed outside, and who would have taken him captive had it not been for the grace and providence of God, and for the help of Sultan Saif, who drove him to our house in his car. That day, my father was wounded in the arm. I have a clear memory of him coming home drenched in blood. He didn't tell us about Youssef and Ahlam – a story I first heard from you. My mother also refrained from asking about my father's activities during that period. My father went into his room and my mother attended to him like an experienced doctor. She extracted the bullet – which I have kept to this day – from my father's arm, and then cleaned and cauterised the wound. She was so strong. The love she felt for her husband did not prevent her from doing her duty toward her country, and she urged my father to press on with his defence of Kuwait.

"Watch your step at all times, don't let yourself fall into their hands."

My father smiled at her affectionately. "Are you worried about me?"

"I'm worried the larger group will lose its nerve if anything happens to their top man."

"Pray for me, Noura."

"God be with you, Dawoud." Ahlam's rescue was one of the noblest and most heroic things my father had done and the one that was closest to your heart, as you used to say. After telling me that story, you said to me: "You know, Abdel Aziz, I dream about a man who'd be as brave as Dawoud Abdel Aziz." This kind of man, I replied to you at the time, had gone the way of dinosaurs and mammoths.

* Najat al-Saghira is a famous Egyptian singer

From the author's novel *Sijeen al-Maraya* (Prisoner of Mirrors), published by Arab Scentific Publishers, Beirut 2012

Andrew C Long reviews
Throwing Sparks
by Abdo Khal

Translated by Maia Tabet, Michael K. Scott
Bloomsbury Qatar Foundation Publishing,
2013, Pbk, 368 pages,
ISBN: 978-9992179093

Redemption in Jeddah

Abdo Khal's award-winning novel, *Throwing Sparks*, is a welcome addition to the growing list of English translations of recent Arabic fiction. Khal won the prestigious International Prize for Arabic Fiction for the original Arabic edition, *Tarmi bi Sharar*, published in 2010, even though the novel was banned in his native Saudi Arabia and several other Arab countries. Indeed, Bloomsbury Qatar Foundation Publishing, the publisher of the English edition, are to be commended as this kind of cultural intervention can only improve the Arab-Western encounter of the last two decades. Moreover, the translation of fiction – novels – is also significant as the genre is the quintessential Western cultural form, and yet it is in non-Western contexts, and especially the Arab and Muslim world, that writers and readers have brought a new vitality to the genre. And, of course, that this is a novel by a Saudi writer, who is known and respected in the Arab world, and that it is a novel set in a Saudi city – Jeddah – in the last decade, are notable aspects as we in the West know so little about the literary and filmmaking scene in the Saudi kingdom, other than perhaps Abdulrahman Munif's magnificent *Cities of Salt* trilogy.

Throwing Sparks traces the life stories of Tarek Fadel and his small group of friends, especially two other boys, Issa and Osama, as they grow up together in a slum district of Jeddah known as "the Firepit" and move on to lives in very different circumstances. All of them are children of abject poverty with abusive or absent parents, and all are victims of sexual violence, and victimizers as well. And so, barely beyond adolescence, it would seem that their collective fortune has turned when one of the boys, Issa, meets the family of a wealthy and powerful man whom they will later know as "the Master", and the three friends are miraculously lifted from the abject poverty of the Firepit into the opulence and vulgar decadence of "the Palace".

Though Issa and Osama figure in the plot and the narrative as a whole, and other friends, relatives and enemies dominate particular chapters, the novel is centered around the life of Tarek, as it is to some extent both a kind of confessional novel and a profession of faith, and so written in the first person. Once inside the Palace walls Tarek quickly found a place in the Master's household as a Punisher, a professional rapist who specializes in sodomizing men, enemies or rivals, or simply victims of the Master's aberrant whims. Apparently, due to his endowment – his nickname in the Firepit was "the Hammer" – and the skill and energy with which he carried out his assignments, he quickly earned the trust and respect of the Master who asked him to assemble a team of professional rapists, the Punisher Squad, which he led before dissolving them as the Master's whimsy drew his attention elsewhere, notably to a woman with a history, Maram.

Throwing Sparks is chronological, with much of the narrative set in the Palace or the time the boys were there together. Khal frequently uses flashbacks to the early years in the Firepit to provide background on our characters and explain their motivations for actions taken later, in the Palace period. And so we are introduced to other characters, such as Tarek's shrewish Aunt Khayriyyah whom he forcibly moves from the Firepit to his villa and later violently assaults and mutilates, and notably Tahani, the neighborhood girl whom Tarek and Osama both loved and wooed, leading to calamity for all concerned. Indeed, even Maram is tied back into the narrative, as she is woman with roots and a story, or rather a score to settle, intertwined with those early years in the Firepit. For the most part Khal is deft with the release of information, developing the plot and building the tension, as the separate vignettes converge within the last few chapters. However, there are moments of repetition, from chapter, to chapter of information which we already know, though this might be a deliberate device on the part of the author, hinting at the oral traditions of Arabic storytelling.

Yet it is two women, the Master's mistress, Maram, and his sister, Mawdie, the beloved of Issa, who pull the plot along its course towards the disastrous conclusion. As much as this is a novel about men – including sex between men, as most of the male characters are either bisexual or homosexual, or, as the narrator tells us, simply desire "boys" – women and the suffering they must endure are a feature of *Throwing Sparks*. Though Khal does much to encourage our empathy for the various women of the novel, and though the novel clearly condemns the vile treatment of women and their secondary status in Saudi Arabia, one gets the sense that women are set on a pedestal, which is not necessarily progressive. Still, before we conflate the narrator and Khal we should remember that this is a novel which renders the consciousness of a depraved man, and to some, that way of thinking about women is consistent with misogynistic violence. As for sex and sexuality, there is no sensuousness in the world of this novel. Sex is about conquest and subordination, while love is almost always discussed without sex, as a kind of transcendent sentiment.

Far from love and transcendence, *Throwing Sparks* might be described as a novel about torture as the narrator is a "punisher" and nothing more, and as there are brief descriptions of "punishment" scenes, but I think this is a shortsighted, if not an incorrect reading of the novel. As with the sex scenes, there is minimal detail offered about the torture scenes, allowing Khal to sidestep any accusations of cheap salaciousness or worse. Indeed, torture – rape – is consistent with the larger themes of the novel, that is, the depravity which flows from a particular kind of social and political order, and so it is apt rather than gratuitous that our narrator is a torturer, and the

Abdo Khal

epigraph of the last section of the novel, "The Second Threshold", emphasizes this point linking such politics to terrorism.

Moreover, while there are many 20th-century Western novels about torture, or confessions of torturers, or torture victim narratives, in terms of recent Arabic fiction it is Elias Khoury's brilliant and terrifying novel, *Yalo*, that comes to mind. Unlike the latter, which offers us a claustrophobic realist urban context, that is, Achrafieh and the Mathaf-Museum crossing areas of Christian East Beirut, *Throwing Sparks* is not really a realist novel, as its two spaces do not figure in the narrative as in other novels, taking us back to the British and French novels of the 19th century, or Mahfouz's Cairo. Khal's use of social space is appropriate since the slum space

عبده خال

ترمي بشرر...

منشورات الجمل
رواية

*Arabic front cover of Spewing Sparks –
Tarmi bi Sharar*

of the Firepit is opposed by the palace of the Master, as a kind of dialectic within which the characters emerge, and that is what he chooses to emphasize. Indeed, the contradictions of their lives in the Firepit, that is, various reprehensible crimes, fully unfold outside the area, during their adult lives in the Palace. We might read these crimes as sins, or a virus which can never be fully treated, or we can see the Palace and its relative freedoms – in a loose use of this word here – as a space which permits the un-folding or, in a biological sense, the festering of these crimes and the narrative consequences.

Undoubtedly *Throwing Sparks* was banned for political reasons, though we might assume obscenity was probably cited by the au-thorities in the countries concerned. In some ways Khal's novel is reminiscent of a recent Lebanese film, Marc Abi Rached's "Help" (2009) which follows a prostitute as she escapes from the murder-ous clutches of a Lebanese warlord/businessman, aided by a gay cross-dressing roommate and a homeless orphan Shia boy, Ali. The allegory of Lebanon and Lebanese politics is unmistakable and the film upset many local viewers and was banned shortly thereafter, as there were scenes which vaguely depicted a ménage à trois as well as the breasts of the main actress, Joanna Andraos. I suggest that the film and this novel are politically dangerous as they represent politics in the Middle East in its rawest form, zero degree, that of gangster capitalism. Whether they are warlords or "Masters", the ruling elite are finally businessmen. There is no longer politics as we might normally think of it, with parties and collective struggle, and there is no longer class politics. This is a world of the funda-mental struggle between master, or the Master, and slave. It is a stark world, yet not a primitive one, but, rather the late modern present of many countries. Khal, who studied Political Science, is keen to point out this conundrum as the Master is a masterful businessman who seizes public assets for himself, such as water front properties, ruining the local fishermen, and uses the offices of the State to entice and then financially ruin his rivals, and of course manipulates the stock market on a daily basis. Such crude violations and abuse of power are reminiscent of well-known regimes in North Africa and the Middle East, and fueled the protests and movements of the Arab Spring of the last three years.

This last point presents us with an interesting conundrum as the novel is indisputably Islamic in tone and content: Khal was a street preacher earlier in his life and the Arabic title of the novel is *Spewing Sparks as Big as Castles* and derived from the Qur'an. Still, the novel form is a curious thing as it forces all of us to squeeze our experiences into a frame which was created long ago in the 18th and 19th centuries. And so we find ourselves, whatever our faith or secular commitments, or wherever we are, sleepwalking – or rather writing – in the steps of John Bunyan and his 17th century proto novel, *The Pilgrim's Progress*. Indeed, as Tarek grows more disillusioned with his life and "job" at the Palace, and as his friends die or disappear into their obsessions, while we might expect a final act of vengeance, and a gratifying murder of the Master – at least for an American readership – instead we have a spiritual conclusion as the novel ends in the Salvation Mosque in the midst of a prayer led by Ibrahim, Tarek's half-brother, and while it is somewhat ambiguous, it is nonetheless uplifting in its simplicity and humility of spirit.

And perhaps this surprising conclusion is the most eloquent and moving moment in *Throwing Sparks*, for whereas many authors might offer blood and closure – revolution and/or revenge – this is a novel of politics and faith which proposes something more open-ended and transcendent.

Mona Zaki reviews

The Mehlis Report
by Rabee Jaber

Translated by
Kareem James Abu-Zeid

New York: New Directions, 2013.
ISBN 978-0-8112-2064-4

A city
haunted

Beirut awaits the preliminary findings of the Mehlis Report – the UN investigation into the assassination of Lebanon's Prime Minister, Rafik Hariri. On February 14th, 2005, two thousand pounds of explosives shook the city and the confidence of its people. The Mehlis Report – released almost eight months later – would put all rumours and fears to rest.

Narrator, Samaan Yarid, is a Beiruti architect who cannot imagine living anywhere else. In his account of homes, streets, people, eateries and girlfriends nothing is rushed – Samaan is a man comfortable with the space around him. Like Orhan Pamuk's Istanbul, Beirut joins the list of Mediterranean cities described in loving detail, from Venetian skylights to the lofty ceilings of old houses oak trees and grandfather clocks. All bear witness to the vision of enterprising Levantines. Samaan is a tireless walker who knows Beirut's streets and its short cuts – a day in his life captures the unrushed way of life in which people enjoy their food and their friends. Jaber shares with Pamuk a longing for an older way of life that, for him, represents culture at its best.

The fear of civil war, however, is never far away and, as the city anxiously awaits the Mehlis report, this fear appears real. Beirut is tense (skittish is a word often used) and haunted by memories of

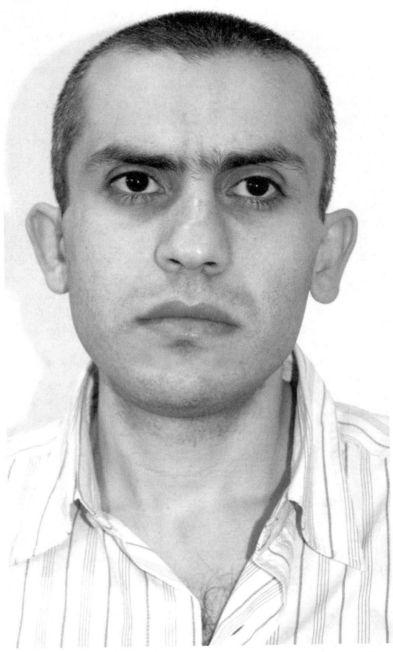

Rabee Jaber

conflict. We learn that Samaan's younger sister was kidnapped and left dead on the dividing line between East and West Beirut. Despite tragedy, people move on. Could the report on the latest high profile victim reignite conflict? Will Mehlis have the courage to indict the perpetrators behind the assassination? Will the truth set anyone free?

Described as a thriller, the resemblance of the title to that of the neo-noir science movie "Minority Report" might be a coincidence. Suspense grips the narrative from the first pages and soon another voice begins to track Samaan's tireless roaming which is also a symptom of his anxiety.

Just over half way through the novel, we learn that this second voice belongs to his dead sister, Josephine, narrating her capture and "crossing over". Souls in the next life, according to Jaber, spend their time in a library, poring over books in large reading rooms. Josephine writes compulsively to exorcise her painful end. Like her brother, her longing keeps her attached to the city. We are told that there are two types of books: real ones and ones produced by those who do not read (which are not worth reading!). The only torment described in Jaber's afterlife takes place in the enclave reserved for killers who live in huts made of bones and swim in pools of blood as their thirst sucks the tears from their eyes.

The accounts of Samaan and Josephine are punctuated by the events of the civil war. In Jaber's work, fear is experienced as an afterthought once we are out of the danger zone of war. The obsessive construction boom (Rafik Hariri was, after all, a business tycoon) came at the cost of demolishing Beirut's identity.

Without revealing how the novel ends, each telling of the Lebanese civil war remains a deeply personal account — *The Mehlis Report* joins other works, such as Hoda Barakat's *The Tiller of Water*, in depicting a city haunted by death and destruction. Kareem James Abu-Zeid has faithfully maintained the pace of this complex work of fiction. In Jaber's first novel to be translated into English, the depth of his prose has been well served through Abu-Zeid's meticulous efforts.

Read these authors online with a digital subscription from iTunes or Exact Editions

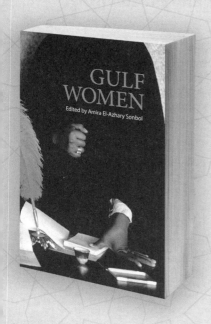

Gulf Women

Edited by Amira El-Azhary Sonbol

A groundbreaking collection of essays that provides a greater understanding of the history of the Gulf and the Arab world, as well as the history of Muslim women.

ISBN 9789992142684 | 464 pages | PB | £19.99
Also available as an e-book

Arab Women In Arab News
Old Stereotypes and New Media

Amal Al-Malki, David Kaufer, Suguru Ishizaki and Kira Dreher

When Arab women are portrayed in Western media, they are typically veiled and voiceless, their words spoken for them in captions and voice-overs. But where do Arab women stand in current Arab news? For the first time, this book provides systematic answers to these and other questions.

'Turning the representational lens inward to the Arab world Amal Al-Malki et al reveal complex and riveting images of Arab women in Arab news...' *Suad Joseph, Professor of Anthropology and Women and Gender Studies, University of California, Davis, US*

ISBN 9789992179116 | 496 pages | PB | £25
Also available as an e-book

Paul Starkey reviews

That Smell and Notes from Prison

by Sonallah Ibrahim
translated by Robyn Creswell
New Directions, New York, 2013.
Pbk, 120 pp, $15.95, £11.99.
ISBN 978 0 8112 2036 1

Capturing the spirit

With so much worthwhile Arabic literature remaining untranslated, "retranslations" of Arabic novels usually strike one as something of a luxury. So the publication of a new translation of Sonallah Ibrahim's slim volume, *Tilka al-Ra'iha*, which first appeared in Arabic in 1966 before being quickly confiscated, comes as rather a shock. Both Ibrahim's work itself, which is widely regarded as heralding the arrival of the so-called 'Generation of the Sixties', and Denys Johnson-Davies's original English translation (*The Smell of It And Other Stories*, originally published in 1971), are seminal works in their respective fields, and the complex publishing history of the work – the English translation actually appeared before the full text of the Arabic became generally available – bears witness to the tortuous constraints of censorship that Egyptian writers of the day (and later) have had to grapple with. In retrospect, the work has been seen both as foreshadowing the humiliation of the Arab defeat in the 1967 Six-Day War and as ushering in a new mood in modern Arabic writing,

Why, then, this new translation? In his lively and thought-provoking introduction, Robyn Creswell explains that he finds Denys Johnson-Davies's original translation (now out of print) too "elegant", and that it fails to convey the deliberately bald and "aggressively unliterary" style of the original. In Johnson-Davies's version, Creswell explains: "Ibrahim's lower-middle-class characters speak a plummy version of English and the unbroken block of the original Arabic text – a layout that fits the stream-of-consciousness narrative – is transformed into tidy paragraphs and indented dialogue." Creswell's

Photo: Samuel Shimon

version aims to redress this balance and recapture something of the spirit and mood of Ibrahim's original Arabic, the deliberately sparse and unadorned style of which reflects the monotony of his Cairo protagonist's life.

I have to confess that I personally have never found Denys Johnson-Davies's "plummy English" any more of a hindrance to enjoyment than the incongruous fusha spoken by many of Ibrahim's (and other Arab authors') characters. Be that as it may, however, there is no doubt that Creswell has produced an effective translation, which successfully captures the spirit of Ibrahim's original text — a text that clearly reflected the mood of many contemporary Egyptian in-

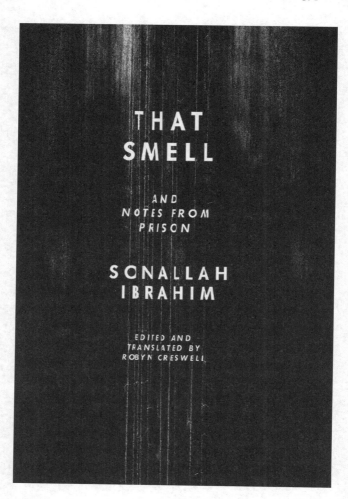

THAT
SMELL

AND
NOTES FROM
PRISON

SONALLAH
IBRAHIM

EDITED AND
TRANSLATED BY
ROBYN CRESWELL

Fiction from **Kuwait**

tellectuals, but which also disturbed and shocked many at the time of first publication, not only for its deliberately "unliterary" use of the literary language, but also for its explicit sexual references.

In addition to his new translation of *Tilka al-Ra'iha*, Creswell has also included in his volume an English translation of Sonallah Ibrahim's own introduction to the 1986 Arabic version of his work; a wide-ranging introduction of his own; and an English translation of excerpts from Ibrahim's *Yawmiyyat al-Wahat* (Oasis Diaries), published in Arabic in book form in 2004, and here renamed *Notes from Prison*. Creswell's introduction provides the reader with useful background information, not only on the literary aspects of the work, but also on the political context, including, centrally, the ups and downs under Nasser of the Egyptian Communist Party, which has played a central part in Sonallah Ibrahim's life and career as a writer.

Perhaps even more valuable and revealing, however, are the excerpts from *Yawmiyyat al-Wahat*, written between 1962 and 1964, during the last two years of Ibrahim's imprisonment for political reasons. Originally written as secret notebooks and subsequently transferred to Turkish Bafra-brand cigarette papers to be smuggled out of prison, these diaries are inevitably somewhat disjointed, but they serve both as a powerful indicator of the centrality of literature in Sonallah Ibrahim's life and as a commentary on the debates about realism that remained a live issue for Egyptian writers of the day.

For this volume Creswell has selected passages amounting to roughly one fifth of the full Arabic publication that he considers most relevant to the reading of *Tilka al-Ra'iha*; for many readers, they will probably whet the appetite for more.

Robyn Creswell and New Directions are to be congratulated for making this new material available to English readers, and for reviving interest in Sonallah Ibrahim's ground-breaking work though this new translation.

Paul Starkey's book, *Sun' Allah Ibrahim: Rebel with a Pen*, is due to be published by Edinburgh University Press in 2014.

Fiction from **Kuwait**

Susannah Tarbush reviews

Earth Weeps, Saturn Laughs
by Abdulaziz Al Farsi

Translated by Nancy Roberts
AUC Press, Cairo, April 2013
pbk 240pp, $17.95, £13.50.
ISBN: 978 977 416 590 0

Khalid meets his muse

O mani writer Abdulaziz Al Farsi's debut novel opens with a young man, Khalid Bakhit, waking the people of his village at night when he shouts a lament from his balcony. He claims his song was written by a poet from Saturn: "Alone I was, O homeland of mine, and you with me, travelling in me, living within me . . ."

Khalid has recently returned to the village after eight years in the city as a university student and then government employee. In the city he had enjoyed a rhapsodic affair with a woman named Abir, but after making a shocking discovery about his lover he has re-

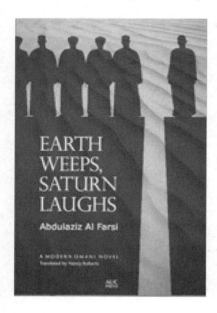

treated to the village on unpaid leave.

Some villagers are angered by Khalid's return and by his strange behaviour. "Khalid Bakhit has made our life hell" says one. Another says he may intend to bring development, and "we don't want development that destroys the goodwill among us and makes us like city folk . . . the more developed we get, the more we grow apart."

There are suspicions about Khalid's meetings with young men and the books with "white pages" he gives them. In his younger days

Abdulaziz Al Farsi

he had been through a hard-line religious phase, but there are rumours he became an atheist at university.

Adding to the disquiet is the shadow over Khalid's family. His father had died horribly of alcoholism, and this and other scandals lurk around Khalid's powerful grandfather Zahir. "That entire family is a sinkhole of corruption in this village, and we've been suffering on their account for years," complains fisherman Suhayl al-Jamra al-Khabitha. But Zahir has the support of hereditary village leader Mihyan Ibn Khalaf, a builder of traditional mud houses, and of the wise, fair-minded merchant Walad Sulaymi. When a council meeting is held to discuss what should be done about Khalid, Zahir slyly deflects the conversation to the imminent arrival in the village of young Bangladeshi religious scholar Alam al-Din.

Khalid decides "to concern myself with the village's crazy secrets, and with discovering what it had left to posterity in time gone by". He passes through painful times as he learns of the reason for his father's alcoholism. The novel combines tragedy with humour and transcendent joy. Poetry, legends and jokes mingle in an engaging narrative, replete with stories.

Earth Weeps, Saturn Laughs poses challenges for the translator. It has an ambitious structure, with each of its 24 chapters told by one of seven first-person narrators. The text includes frequent wordplay, examples of which are explained in the glossary. There are extracts from the Qur'an, for which Roberts deploys passages from the classic translations by A J Arberry, Abdullah Yusuf Ali and Muhammad Assad. Several of the characters have comic nicknames: Suhayl al-Jamra al-Khabitha's name, for instance, means Suhayl Anthrax.

The seven narrators include Khalid and his muse and confidant, the whimsical Saturnine Poet who happened upon the village by chance while chasing a poem. The other narrators are Walad Sulaymi, Mihyan ibn Khalaf, the black youth Khadim Walad al-Sayl who grew up in Mihyan's house, Suhayl al-Jamra al-Khabitha, and Ayda, a free-spirited beauty who has long craved Khalid's attention.

Ayda is the village's only female university student. She sees

Khalid as a hero and remembers how he led the university's first student demonstration and how there was a huge popular demonstration after he brought together students and the poor.

As village leader Mihyan has a meeting-house where the villagers gather. In one of the novel's main plotlines, Suhayl al-Jamra al-Khabitha plots with others to get Mihyan replaced as village leader. As part of this Suhayl instigates the building of an alternative meetinghouse, which Zahir denounces as the "Council of Harm". The gentle Mihyan is sensitively drawn. Modern houses built by workers brought from overseas have sprung up alongside the village's traditional mud houses, but Mihyan loves the pleasurable sensations and smells of working with mud. Khadim's second name "Walad al-Sayl" means "son of the flood". Fifteen years earlier, he had been found as a boy of three in a copper-coloured washbasin after a terrible flood in Mihyan's wife and young son were drowned and Mihyan agreed to take the child under his wing. As the only black person in the village Khadim endured the traditional racist discrimination in which blacks are seen as slaves; this legacy of slavery is one of the novel's dark undercurrents.

Earth Weeps, Saturn Laughs is an impressive achievement for its author, who was born in the Omani coastal town of Shinas in 1976. Al Farsi combines a career as a writer with that of a senior specialist in oncology at the National Oncology Centre of the Royal Hospital in Muscat.

Al Farsi began writing in 1998, and is the author of six collections of short stories and two works of biography. *Earth Weeps, Saturn Laughs* was first published in 2007 in Arabic. An excerpt from it, translated by William Granara, was first published in *Banipal 32* (Summer 2008), so it is satisfying to now see the complete novel in English translation five years later.

Nancy Roberts has produced an inspired, lyrical translation which will surely further enhance her reputation. The translator of some ten Arabic novels, she won the Arkansas Arabic Manuscript Translation Award for her translation of Syrian author Ghada Samman's *Beirut '75*, published by the University of Arkansas Press in 1995. In 2008 the judges of the Saif Ghobash Banipal Prize for Arabic Literary Translation commended her translation of Egyptian writer Salwa Bakr's novel *The Man from Bashmour* (AUC Press, 2007).

Margaret Obank reviews

Divorce Islamic Style
by Amara Lakhous
Translated from the Italian
by Ann Goldstein
Europa Editions, USA, 2012
Pbk, 192pp, $15, £9.99 ISBN: 9781609450663

Rome's Little Cairo under observation

Amara Lakhous's second novel in English translation is even more irreverent than the first – *Clash of Civilizations Over an Elevator in Piazza Vittorio*, which won Italy's prestigious Flaiano Prize. He is a brilliantly satirical comic author, whose sharp nose for the absurd results in prejudice and stereotype, backwardness and outdated customs being pricked at every opportunity and deflated to loud guffaws.

How one looks at the other is a central issue for Amara Lakhous and in this novel he also looks at how different beliefs and outlooks can be tolerated and understood, and. His strength as a writer lies in describing how every-day scenarios affect different ethnic communities, juxtaposing one against the other to expose the irrationality, the proposterousness, the backwardness of prejudices, myths or customs that lead people to maintain certain positions or have certain beliefs. Born and raised in Algeria and living in Italy, he complimented his philosophy degree from the University of Algiers with a second degree in cultural anthropology from Rome's University La Sapienza.

Divorce Islamic Style is itself multi-faceted – it is as thorough as a documentary, as rounded and meticulously devised as a Hercule Poirot thriller, as hilarious and revealing as an Oscar Wilde situation drama or a Shakespearean comedy, and all the while being, in addition, a 21st-century call for tolerance, freedom, multi-identity being a norm, and an important contribution to putting Islamopho-

bia firmly in its racist gutter. Its multiple characteristics also include fascinating digressions such as one about Garibaldi's year-long stay in Tunisia under an alias in order to escape the death penalty in Italy for insurrection.

The action is set in Rome like Lakhous's first novel, but this time in the Little Cairo quarter that houses a large Arab immigrant population, where aliases abound on a number of levels and nothing is what it seems. Amara Lakhous is a visual, filmic writer, not just through his vivid characterisations and descriptions, but also by the film-star nicknames/aliases he hands out. Perhaps for this reason the title is *Divorce Islamic Style*, recalling the popular film "Divorce Italian Style" starring Marcello Mastroianni. The young Sicilian lawyer Christian Mazzari, who becomes unemployed Tunisian immigrant, Issa, with a "crummy mustache" and "new identity papers", is no match for James Bond or Donny Brasco in his guise as an anti-terrorist spy, recruited to spy on ordinary Arab Muslims who are apparently planning a "large-scale attack".

Akhram, the owner of the call centre cum café where the members of the so-called "terrorist cells" meet – according to Captain Judas, Christian's intelligence chief – is the spitting image of John Belushi. Pizza-maker Ahmed Metwalli becomes Felice and his wife Safia, also from Egypt, is always called Sofia by Italians, who assume she's mispronouncing her own name but concede that it fits her because she looks like Sophia Loren. Christian/Issa and Safia/Sofia become the two narrators, with the chapters of the novel given over alternately to each of them, although Sofia thinks of Issa as the Arab Marcello, after dreaming of Marcello Mastroianni who turns into the young Arab man she keeps glimpsing in the call centre and local library. With this essential device they can give voice to their hidden

Amara Lakhous at the Abu Dhabi International Book Fair in April this year   Photo: Margaret Oba

concerns and dreams, their supposed destinies that are "maktub" (written), their hidden identities and what they really think, while at the same time allowing the action to move uproariously forward to its very surprising denouement. Marriage or living together, divorce – which is at the centre of the action – the veil, headscarves, racism, cosmetic surgery, all are given the Lakhous treatment.

When Safia meets Issa for the first time in her house, towards the end of the action, she thinks how she would much prefer him without the moustache as "it's really out of place". While this is a cue for her critical pronouncement that "for Arabs hair continues to be the symbol of virility and paternal authority", it also smartly links up with Issa's opinion of the mustache at the beginning, having been forced to grow it in order to look the part of a Tunisian immigrant.

A last word of thanks to Ann Goldstein, who has given English readers a fluent and fast-paced brilliant translation. Readers, you have to read this book. It's a great read, with so many striking characters and a surprising – because it is sort of happy-ever-after – denouement that is definitely not what you will be expecting.

Stephen Watts reviews

Poems for the Millennium (Vol. 4): The University of California Book of North African Literature

Edited with Introductions by Pierre Joris and Habib Tengour

University of California Press (Berkeley, LA) 2012.
Pbk 760 pages, ISBN: 9780520273856 $39.95, £27.95. Also hbk $80.00, £55.00, ISBN: 9780520269132 and Adobe PDF E-Book, $39.95, ISBN: 9780520953796

Poetry's vital breath

L et it be said clearly from the outset: this is a remarkable and very beautiful book, a profound and exemplary anthology of the poetries of a culturally expansive Maghreb. Its scope is vast: in time, from Apuleius and Augustine through to the youngest of contemporary Maghrebi poets; in space, widening its arms to include great Arabic and Hebrew poets of al-Andalus and Spanish language poets from Mauritania and Spanish Sahara; in its definition of poetry, to include prose that either has poetry at its heart or that comments on the wider contexts of poetry; in its linguistic cultural range, to include contemporary Arabic, Francophone and Berber/Tamazight writers, but focusing always on varied tradition; in its inclusion of oral texts and strands as the vital breath of all poetry; and in its embrace of both incoming writers and those forced into exile, as part of the wider tradition.

It includes a large number of new, previously unpublished translations, distinguishing it from many other topical, but essentially thinly thought out compilations. This book is not merely here today and gone tomorrow, rather it is an eminently considered accumulation of texts, brought together over more than 25 years by the volume's two editors. It has all the vision and energy of a radically new sense of language and poetry, together with all the solidity and cultural steadfastness of genuine scholarly assemblage. It is, in other words, a superb idea come to fruition at a providentially right time.

It is arranged both linearly and by topos. It works horizontally and vertically at the same time, allowing history to seep and weave

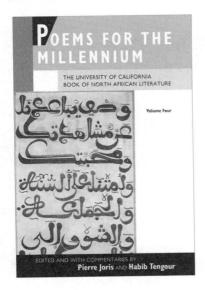

through. It has been assembled as a cluster of themes (A Book of Multiple Beginnings, A Book of Mystics) and a series of historically defined Diwans (The Third Diwan: The Long Sleep and The Slow Awakening; Fourth Diwan: Resistance and Road to Independence), together with titled excursuses into named Oral Traditions. This sweep takes us through from earliest times and texts to the contemporary poetries of Mohammed Bennis, Abdellatif Laâbi and others, although almost two thirds of the anthology's 760 pages are given over to C20th and C21th poetries. It is an anthology that should not be read as filling in a gap in our ignorance, but rather as indicating a source of difference and alerting its English language readers to a different solidity, another regime of cultural viability.

Does it have deficiencies? Every anthology, every spoken or written word must, but they seem few in this case. Many of the poets included deserve wider recognition than the few pages an anthology can provide, but with this book it seems more of a success, provoking us to seek out more. One or two names are absent: of contemporary poets it's surprising not to find Hédi Bouraoui or Soleïman Adel Guémar. No bibliography of existing translations is given and this is a pity. Joris and Tengour's previous joint work, the former's translation of the latter's *Exile Is My Trade* (Black Widow, 2012, and another superb book deserving of wide readership) is not, I think, mentioned, nor are the English translations of Tahar Ben Jelloun, Nabile Farès and others, or Marilyn Hacker's admittedly very recent books of Amina Said or Rachida Madani, nor *The Selected Poems of Jean Sénac* (Sheep Meadow Press, 2010), a poet the editors praise highly. But I'm wasting words on detail: this is quite simply a superb and exemplary book, one whose achievements far outweigh almost any other anthology of world or zonal poetry I can think of, a model, surely, and yardstick for future anthologies.

Margaret Obank reviews

Sun Bread and Sticky Toffee: Date Desserts from Everywhere

by Sarah Al-Hamad

Interlink Books, April 2013, ISBN: 978-1566569217, 144 pages, illustrated, Size: 21.6 x 2.3 x 27.3 cm

The Bread of the desert

What is it about dates that makes them irresistable? You just have to eat them. So, *Sun Bread and Sticky Toffee: Date Desserts from Everywhere* is a gorgeous treat. Sarah al-Hamad happily discovered that many different communities around the world loved eating puddings and desserts made with dates and decided that it was high time for a book about this phenomenon. She visited many countries, spoke to many people, took incredible photographs and has produced a mouth-watering, colourful and informative journey through the world of date desserts, with a host of easy recipes so that readers can produce their date favourites themselves.

I have to profess a personal interest. Not only is Sarah an old friend, but as I hail from a Northern England family I was already very familiar with date cake, and date and banana loaf – but without the now essential sticky toffee sauce, which was added some time in the 1970s. As small children, my sisters and I would pester my mother to make us date sandwiches and date cake as she regularly bought packets of Lion of Babylon squashed dates, imported from Iraq, with her weekly shop. Much later, when Iraqis themselves started seeking refuge in the UK, dibis, date syrup, was to follow.

Sarah begins her journey in the Gulf, describing her personal connection to the date through her paternal great-grandfather who traded in dates in Iraq and her late grandfather who had a date plantation there, like many Kuwaitis in the early 1900s who owned property and plantations in the south of Iraq. From a young age, having heard that

The author with her book

there were 400 different varieties of Basra dates, I always envisioned the area as a profusion of date plantations. Today, after war, deprivation and relentless devastation, it is a very different picture, with Asia's greatest date production coming from Saudi Arabia — from Al-Hasa oasis with its "3 million cultivated date palms".

This is now one of the world's great producers, after Egypt and Iran.

Sarah al-Hamad's extended introduction to *Sun Bread and Sticky Toffee* is an historical odyssey of the "Amber Nectar", starting 6,000 years ago in Babylon, then Basra – and as a child in Kuwait Sarah would often hear Basra described as "the Gulf's orchard" – then it's off to Egypt, Afghanistan, Sicily, the Silk Road, Crete, Sicily (with the Romans), taking in the Phoenicians who carried date palms to Spain, and particularly Elche, to the Canary Islands, the Balaerics, Malta, and the Levant – Palestine, Lebanon and Syria. And on to North Africa, where Morocco started trading dates with England under Queen Elizabeth I. Then the USA, where California's top two dates were cultivated from the Moroccan medjool and Tunisia's deglet noor dates, and where the town of Indio is the heart of US date country, every February hosting the National Date Festival, and home of the Shields Date Garden, where visitors can see a short film on "The Romance and Sex Life of the Date".

Finally, the odyssey comes full circle back to the Gulf, this time to Al Ain in the United Arab Emirates, the mecca for all date enthusiasts being the annual Liwa Date Festival in early July.

Palms are male or female, and to produce dates the female flowers have to be pollinated. In the absence of bees, pollination by plantation workers every spring ensures rich crops of dates. A famous male palm in California, imported from Arabia in 1912, was responsible for pollinating 400 female palms, "resulting in 3,600,000 off-spring each year".

Among the mouth-watering recipes is the title one, Sun Bread, inspired by an ancient Egyptian recipe. Still a staple loaf today, it is a "dense, fragrant, sweet bread" made with butter, dates, honey, eggs, sweet spices (nutmeg and cinnamon) and chopped almonds, and is best served warm to keep the dates deliciously moist.

There are recipes from Egypt, the Gulf, Iran, Kuwait, Europe, Sudan, USA (Chicago), Canada, India, and from the UK's Lake District; recipes from the Middle Ages to the present-day, recipes that mix date and saffron, date and cardamom, date and sesame, date and ginger, date syrup and tahini, date and rose water, date and ricotta, date and pineapple, date and chocolate, dates and oatmeal, date and caramel, or just dates mashed, chopped, cut, pulverised, puréed, boiled.

Sun Bread and Sticky Toffee packs in an astonishing array of dishes, including flatbreads, nans, scones, loaves, cakes, biscuits, macaroons, flapjacks, cookies, muffins, slices, shortbreads, ma'amoul, brownies, tartlets, cheesecake, torte, custard, crumble, crème brulée, compote, fudge, energy balls, fritters, ice cream, milk shakes, jams, and of course plain and fancy stuffed dates.

Dates, it is clear – grown today from 600 varieties worldwide – will carry on being eagerly eaten, cooked and consumed in every which way and this volume will help ensure that the recipes, as well as the dates, make their journeys from country to country and palate to palate.

FICTION

Return of the Spirit: A Novel by Tawfiq al-Hakim. In this newly translated edition of *Return of the Spirit*, first published in 1933, Hakim's pivotal text comes to life, rendered into fluid English by William Maynard Hutchins. *Return of the Spirit* relates the coming-of-age of Muhsin, a patriotic young Egyptian, ending with events surrounding the 1919 revolution and with Muhsin discovering his literary voice. The daily life and experiences of Muhsin's extended family are vividly, and often humorously, portrayed. Hakim's skill at characterisation in the novel has also been widely praised. In his introduction, in which he reviews both the strengths and weaknesses of the text, Hutchins discusses numerous aspects of the novel, including its detailed portrait of Egyptian society nearly a century ago and the significant role it played in the political development of the country and its literature. Lynne Rienner, Boulder/London, 2012, pbk, 295pp. ISBN 978-1-58826-817-4. CB

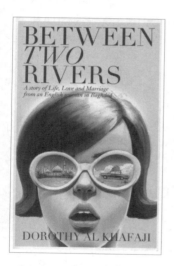

Between Two Rivers by Dorothy Al-Khafaji, sub-titled *A story of Life, Love and Marriage from an English woman in Baghdad*, is a heart-wrenching and beautifully written memoir of an Iraq that is no more. Dorothy and her husband, Zane, who fell in love as students in the UK, want to start a new life in Baghdad for themselves and their tiny baby Summer, and they seize the opportunity when Zane's brother asks him to collect a Mercedes from Germany and drive it to Baghdad.

Dorothy's account of daily life with her extended Iraqi family, preparing meals, going to markets, visits from her parents, having three more children, learning to drive, teaching English at the British Council, is down-to-earth but uncannily vivid – you feel you know the streets and the people she writes about. It's an intimate and loving tribute to Iraq's cosmopolitan era and a fearful glimpse into the brutality and ruthless repression that grew around them with the monopoly on power of Saddam Hussein and the Baathist government. In the end the family had to leave the country, ostensibly going to the UK just for a holiday. Very shortly after arriving back the Iran-Iraq war started. This is a powerful memoir that needs to be published in Arabic. Published by Parthian Books, Wales, UK, 2013. Pbk, 348pp, £8.99. ISBN: 978-1-90894-687-4. MO

King is an epic novel from Riad Nourallah, author and Principal Lecturer at the Diplomatic Academy of London. It tells the story of a prince who is forced to abandon his care-free lifestyle in order to seek revenge for the murder of his father by a rival Arab tribe with Persian connections. Nourallah whisks the reader away on a journey across pre-Islamic Arabia, stretching from Persia to Constantinople, with dramatic and rich descriptions and a plethora of thrilling characters. The novel deals with issues of war and peace, tyranny and freedom and also explores the clashes of cultures and religions during this turbulent historical period. This is Nourallah's second book published with Quartet Books, following his successful novel *The Death of Almustafa*. Quartet Books, London, 2013, hbk, 312 pp. ISBN: 978-0-7043-7318-1. AR

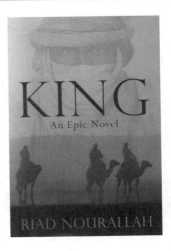

Kalila and Dimna: Fables of Conflict and Intrigue (vol. 2), retold by Ramsay Wood. This is the second volume of translations from Wood, published over thirty years after his first volume appeared in 1980, *Kalila and Dimna: Fables of Friendship and Betrayal*. As in volume one, the stories presented are translated into fluid, dynamic and vibrant English, which nevertheless remains faithful to the original sources. The tales, intended to educate both king and commoner, revolve around the adventures of various different animals from jackals to rams to monkeys. They were originally based on the Indian collection of fables, *The Panchatantra*, and Wood makes use of various different texts in Sanskrit, Syriac, Arabic and Persian. As Michael Wood writes in his introduction, the retold stories are "playful, allusive, richly ambiguous, teasing in their narrative complexity and yet deceptively clear in their resolutions." Illustrated by G. M. Whitworth and with an introduction by Michael Wood. Medina Publishing Ltd, Isle of Wight, 2011, pbk, 240pp. ISBN: 9780 95670 8106. CB

POETRY

Alone Together by Mishka Mojabber Mourani and Aida Yacoub Haddad. This unusual collection of poetry is the result of two decades of correspondence between Mishka Mojabber Mourani, who lives in Beirut and writes in English, and Aida Y. Haddad, who lives in Washington DC and writes in Arabic. The book opens with two letters, which the women address to one another, looking

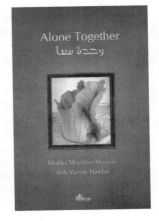

back over their long dialogue with one another, which has continued intermittently over the years. The rest of the work is devoted to poems in English and Arabic, with accompanying translations, echoing the conversations, reflections and experiences shared by the two friends. As Mourani writes in her letter to Haddad: "We have navigated the seas of war and loss of many sorts, and our ports of call have lacked permanence. We have assumed identities and abandoned them. Perhaps one of our chats – this collection here in this book – will shed some light." Kutub, Beirut, 2012, pbk, 204pp, ISBN: 978-9953-554-16-7. CB

NON-FICTION

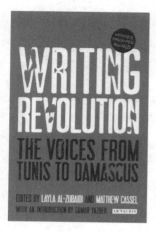

Writing Revolution: The voices from Tunis to Damascus, edited by Layla Al-Zubaidi and Matthew Cassel. This new anthology from I.B. Taurus presents a series of first-person accounts from those who participated in or witnessed the momentous events of the Arab Spring. With contributions from Bahrain, Saudi Arabia, Syria, Egypt, Yemen, Libya, Algeria and Tunisia, the collection offers a broad and diverse picture of the recent changes in the region through a number of creative literary voices. In her introduction, Samar Yazbek describes how the revolutions have called for "a writing forged in the present moment" and the short essays published in this volume certainly provide this. As Yazbek writes, they are a mixture of "subjective experience and objective reportage", mixing humour, horror, sadness and hope. Translated from the French by Georgina Collins and from the Arabic by Robin Moger. I.B. Taurus & Co., London, 2013, pbk, 208pp. ISBN: 9781 78076 5402. CB

Seeking Palestine: New Palestinian Writing on Exile and Home, edited by Penny Johnson and Raja Shehadeh, with contributions from Mourid Barghouti, Mischa Hiller, Fady Joudah and Adania Shibli among others. This collection of essays captures the challenges facing Palestinians today, both those who live within the occupied territories and those abroad. Honest, humorous, politically charged and intimate, the anthology emerged from Palfest, the Palestinian literary festival whose participants include authors from all over the world. Through dialogue amongst writers from Palestine and abroad, the idea for such a text came into being. Penny Johnson writes expressively in her introduction: "it seemed very much like our writers were conversing with each other – and with Palestinian writers before them – exchanging memories, reflections, an occasional joke or a poignant moment of sorrow, like friends on a summer night

SEEKING PALESTINE

New Palestinian Writing
on Exile and Home

EDITED BY PENNY JOHNSON AND RAJA SHEHADEH

in the cool hills of Palestine." Olive Branch Press, Massachusetts. Pbk, 202pp. ISBN: 978-1-56656-906-4. CB.

In the House Un-American is a new novel from Israeli-born American poet and author Benjamin Hollander. The novel, comprised of various genres and historical lenses, questions the idea of American values and identity, and explores the notion of being an "Un-American" immigrant. Politically and culturally poignant, the novel tracks the constant evolution of what it means to be an "authentic" American, from the McCarthy era of the House of Un-American Activities Committee up to the present day. The protagonist of the novel, Carlos ben Carlos Rossman, a Puerto-Rican Jew with Middle Eastern ancestry, arrives in New York in the 1950s and leads the reader on an absurdist journey from the Spanish Golden Age to the Statue of Liberty, providing a prophetic vision for a new relationship between Islam and the American. Stimulating, witty and replete with clever wordplay, this novel provides an interesting perspective on the treatment of immigrants in Hollander's adopted country. Clockroot Books, Massachusetts. Pbk, 150pp, ISBN: 978-1-56656-927-9. AR

A Comprehensive Dictionary of the Middle East is a thoroughly researched dictionary, written and compiled by playwright, journalist and historian Dilip Hiro. As a specialist in South Asia, Central Asia and the Middle East in particular, Hiro has created a must-have reference for all those interested in this fascinating region. The dictionary is easy to use, comprehensive and clearly written, providing information on a wide variety of Middle Eastern topics ranging from culture and history, politics and religion to language and literature. He covers important current affairs such as the Arab Spring, Arab-Israeli wars and regional conflicts, whilst also examining religious sects, tourist destinations and ethnic groups. Olive Branch Press, Massachusetts. Pbk, 756pp. ISBN 978-1-56656-904-0. AR

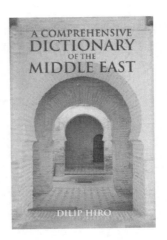

Pastoral in Palestine is a detailed account of literary critic, photographer and professor emeritus Neil Hertz's experience of living in Ramallah, Palestine, in 2011. Whilst teaching at the Abu Dis campus of Al-Quds University, Hertz sent a series of reports back to friends and colleagues detailing all aspects of life in the Occupied Territories of the West Bank. This book is a collection of these reports, and whilst Hertz openly admits that he was unable to experience the horrors of Gaza or the refugee camps, his time spent in Ramallah has provided him

with an interesting insight into life in the Occupied Territories. Published by Prickly Paradigm Press, this book is illustrated throughout with poignant, full-colour photographs taken by Hertz himself. Prickly Paradigm Press, Chicago, pbk, 126pp. ISBN 978-0984-20103-7. AR

Renaissance Emir: A Druze Warlord at the Court of the Medici, by T.J. Gorton. This vibrant biography brings a little known Druze prince of the seventeenth century to English readers for the first time. In fluid prose, Gordan relays the life of Fakhr ad-Din as he struggles against the Ottoman

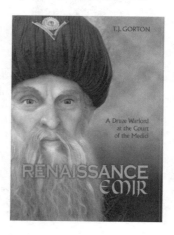

Empire at the pinnacle of its power. Beginning in 1613 in Mount Lebanon, the work follows the rebellious prince into exile with the Medici in Florence in the wake of his defeat by the crushing Ottoman army. Whilst there, the prince plots and plan to unite a great army which he will lead into battle against the Ottomans. Both gripping and informative, Gordan has succeeded in transforming Fakhr ad-Din's remarkable life into a gripping read and depicting the period in which he lived in colourful detail. The biography is based on translations of contemporary sources in Arabic and other languages. Quartet Books, London, 2013, hbk, 226pp, ISBN 978-0-7043-7297-9. CB

A Month by the Sea: Encounters in Gaza by Dervla Murphy. From one of

the most celebrated of travel writers, Irish author Dervla Murphy, comes this frank and insightful account of a month spent in Gaza in the summer of 2011 when the author had just entered her eightieth year. While there, Murphy met and grew close to Palestinians from all walks of life: liberals and Islamists, Hamas and Fatah supporters, rich and poor. In addition to relaying her personal encounters in tender and often humorous detail, Murphy closely and intelligently analyses the effects of isolation on the Gaza community and how it can lead to an increase in both patriarchal and radical beliefs. She also casts her critical gaze on Western and Israeli attitudes to the region. *A Month by the Sea* is a crucial read for all those wishing to understand better the reality of life in Gaza and is beautifully narrated by this experienced and perceptive travel writer. Eland Publishing Ltd, London, 2013, hbk, 224pp. ISBN: 978-1906011475. CB

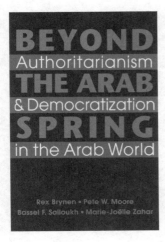

Beyond the Arab Spring: Authoritarianism and Democratization in the Arab World, by Rex Brynen, Pete W. Moore, Bassel F. Salloukh, and Marie-Joëlle Zahar. This collection of essays covers topics ranging from Electoral Politics to the New Arab Media and considers all regions of the Arab World. The four authors draw upon their dialogue with one another and individual wide knowledge of the region to put together an insightful and thought-provoking volume which addresses both the forces which have sustained authoritarianism in the region and the roots of popular mobilization. The book contains an extensive bibliography and will be useful to students, researchers and anyone interested in delving deeper into the past, present and future of the Arab World. Syracuse University Press, USA, 2012, 349pp, ISBN 978-1-58826-878-5. CB

COOKERY

The Gaza Kitchen: A Palestinian Culinary Journey by Laila El-Haddad and Maggie Schmitt is a full-colour cookbook that delivers a warm and intimate picture of daily life in the Gaza Strip. Complete with stunning photography of cooks, kitchens, farms and markets, *The Gaza Kitchen* offers over 120 recipes that reflect the sights, smells and flavours of Gazan home-cooking. Whilst readers may be familiar with Middle Eastern dishes that are now known around the world, like falafel, hummus and kebabs, this book explores the traditional home-foods that are almost never found in restaurants.

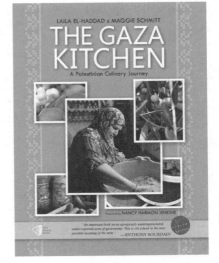

Far more than just a cookbook, what makes this collaborative project so important is the inclusion of conversations with cooks, farmers and economists providing an extraordinary and rare glimpse into daily life for the 1.7 million Palestinians living in Gaza. By seamlessly blending clear, concise recipes with poignant personal stories, *The Gaza Kitchen* brings the territory and its people to life. Just World Books, Virginia, 2013, pbk, 140 pages, ISBN-13: 978-1935982234. AR

The Sheikh Zayed Book Awards Ceremony for 2013 took place at the Abu Dhabi National Exhibition Centre in the presence of dignitaries, prominent public figures, and members of Arab and international literary circles.

Secretary-General of the Sheikh Zayed Book Award, Dr Ali Bin Tamim, said: "We have developed the award to continue to strive towards achieving its objectives, to spread regionally and globally from its home, the United Arab Emirates." Meanwhile, winner of Cultural Personality of the Year Award, Sheikh Ahmed Al Tayeb, the Grand Imam of Al-Azhar, described the award as "essential for continuing our path in promoting our culture and heritage . . . knowledge and education will keep us all on the path of moderation, tolerance and peace".

The winners of this year's prizes are: Contribution to the Development of Nations Award – Elizabeth Kassab (Lebanon); Young Author Award – Adil Hadjami (Morocco); Translation Award – Fathi Meskini (Tunisia); Literary and Art Criticism Award – Adbullah Ibrahim (Iraq); Arab Culture in non-Arabic Languages Award – Marina Warner (UK); Publishing and Technology Award – National Council for Culture, Arts and Literature, Kuwait; Cultural Personality of the Year Award – Sheikh Ahmed Al Tayeb of Al-Azhar (Egypt).

For more information, go to:
www.zayedaward.ae

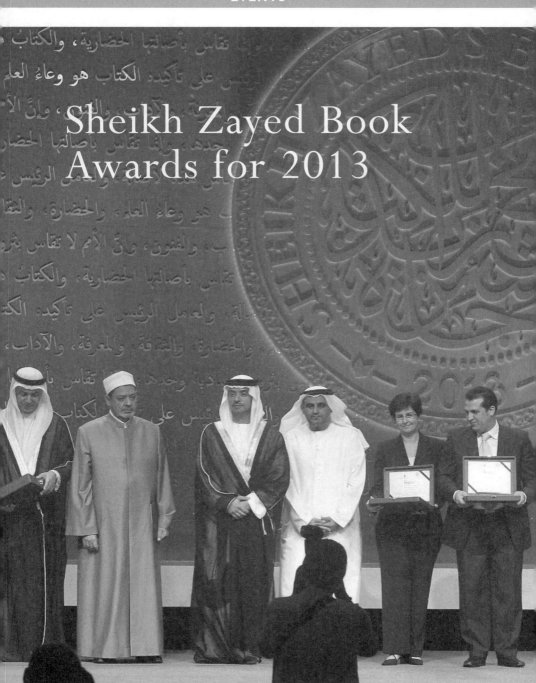

Sheikh Zayed Book
Awards for 2013

Sheikh Hazza Bin Zayed Al-Nahyan presenting the Sheikh Zayed Book Awards

The Casablanca International Book Fair and International Argana Poetry Prize 2013

The 19th International Casablanca Book Fair took place from 29th March – 7th April, 2013. The hundreds of publishers' and booksellers' stands from all over the Arab world, Africa and Europe – with guest of honour Libya – were supported by a comprehensive cultural programme of discussions, talks, readings, book launches and signings. The award ceremony of the Argana International Poetry Prize was held at the Fair for the second year running, the prize awarded to Spanish poet Antonio Gamoneda.

Photo-report by Margaret Obank, who was present at the ceremony and the fair.

Iraqi poet Saadi Youssef reading at the launch of his new collection of poetry

One of the many panel discussions on literary issues at the book fair

On the stage at the award ceremony of the International Argana Poetry (left to right): Poet Hassan Najmi, translator Khalid Raissouni, laureate Antonio Gamoneda, Minister of Culture Mohamed Amine Sbihi, president of the House of Poetry in Morocco Najib Khadouri, and M'hammed Grine, president of the CDG Foundation that sponsors the $12,000 prize

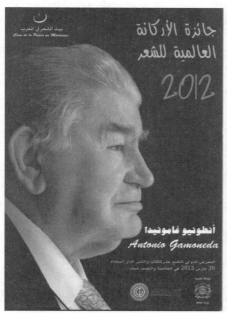

Born in Oviedo, Spain, in 1931, Antonio Gamoneda has won numerous awards for his poetry, including the European Prize for Literature (1993) and the Cervantes Institute Prize for Literature (2006). He is the 7th laureate of the Argana Prize, following Marilyn Hacker, Mahmoud Darwish, Saadi Youssef, Bei Dao and the Moroccan poets Tahar Ben Jelloun and Mohamed Serghini.

Antonio Gamoneda signing a copy of the bilingual Arabic-Spanish collection of his poems, published by the House of Poetry in Morocco for the occasion.

Abu Dhabi International Book Fair

Rachid Boudjedra   Rawi Hage

Algerian author Rachid Boudjedra and Canadian-Lebanese Rawi Hage were among many other Arab authors attending Abu Dhabi's 23rd International Book Fair, 24-29 March, this year. In addition to the 1,025 exhibitors from 50 countries, the cultural programme offered over 250 activities around the twelve halls, with 100 authors and 50 publishing professionals. It included children's events, interviews, panel discussions, readings, book signings, and cookery displays. The second Abu Dhabi International Conference for Translation took place during the Fair and there were also opportunities to meet the winners and shortlisted authors of the International Prize for Arabic Fiction and the Sheikh Zayed Book Awards, both prizes being awarded in conjunction with the fair, IPAF the evening before it started and the latter at the end of the Fair.

Sinan Antoon discussing his IPAF shortlisted novel   *Nasser al-Dhaheri interviewing Amara Lakhous*

Margaret Obank and Jordanian poet Jerius Samawi   *Syrian novelists Nihad Seres and Nabil Suleiman*   *Moroccan author Abdulaziz Errachidi with his new novel*

Heidi Sommerer and Christoph Blum of the Swiss publisher Lenos Verlag at their stand   *Fatima al-Budy, publisher of Dar al-Ain, Cairo, at her stand*

Visitors browsing during the six-day fair

Kuwaiti writer wins 2013 International Prize for Arabic Fiction

Photos courtesy of IPAF

The winner Saud al-Sanousi at the award ceremony in April

The Bamboo Stalk by Kuwaiti author Saud al-Sanousi has won the 2013 International Prize for Arabic Fiction. Born in 1981, al-Sanousi is the youngest writer to win the award. *The Bamboo Stalk* is his second novel. His first, *Prisoner of Mirrors*, published in 2010, is excerpted in this issue of Banipal – *Fiction in Kuwait* (see page 158).

The Bamboo Stalk was selected by the team of five judges as the best work of fiction out of 133 submissions from 15 different Arab countries, all published in 2012.

"A daring work which looks objectively at the phenomenon of foreign workers in Gulf countries", *The Bamboo Stalk* is the story of Issa, the son of a Kuwaiti father and a Filipino mother. In addition to winning $50,000, Saud al-Sanousi is guaranteed an English translation.

All six shortlisted finalists were honoured at the ceremony, with each receiving an award of $10,000. The other short-listed authors are: Mohammed Hasan Alwan, Sinan Antoon, Jana Fawaz Elhassan, Ibrahim Issa and Hussein Al-Wad.

The Prize is supported by the Booker Prize Foundation and funded by the Abu Dhabi Tourism and Culture Authority, which this year marks its first year as the new sponsor of the Prize.

Shortlisted authors Sinan Antoon, Jana Elhassan, Mohammad Hasan Alwan, Ibrahim Essa, Hussain al-Wad and chair of Judges Galal Amin

Jonathan Taylor, Chair of the Board of IPAF Trustees, commented: "The Prize has a history of discovering new voices and we've done that again this year. The judges have been working without fear or favour with their sole objective to identify the best of Arabic fiction published over the last year. We salute a distinguished shortlist and congratulate an outstanding winner."

To date, five of the winning works have secured deals for publication in English, and altogether, winning and shortlisted novels have been translated into over 20 languages. For more information about the prize, go to www.arabicfiction.org.

Fleur Montanaro, the Prize administrator

Sheikh Sultan bin Tahnoon al-Nahyan, chair of the Abu Dhabi Tourism and Culture Authority (TCA) and Jonathan Taylor, chair of the IPAF Board of Trustees

The second Shubbak festival, a celebration of contemporary Arab culture, was launched in London with a reception at the Victoria & Albert Museum on 24 June, where speakers included Alistair Burt, MP, of the Foreign and Commonwealth Office, Mayor of London Boris Johnson and Festival Chair, Omar al-Qattan. The 15-day festival brings together artists, dancers, musicians, playwrights, authors and filmmakers from across the Arab world, offering 50 individual events, including talks and debates, free family outdoor events, film, performance, theatre, fashion, guided tours, as well as nine separate exhibitions, at a number of London venues from Saturday 22nd June to Saturday 6th July.

Pictured right, at the reception, which was sponsored by Barclays plc, are some of the festival's trustees, including Aaron Cezar, David Freeman, Maxime Duda, John Martin, Roxane Zand, director of the Arab British Centre Noreen Abu Oun, Omar al-Qattan and, second from right, the festival's artistic director Eckhard Thiemann.

Photo: Samuel Shimon

Contemporary Arab Fiction took the stage at Asia House in London with Lebanese author Jana Elhassan and Mohammad Hasan Alwan from Saudi Arabia on Thursday evening, 27 June as part of the Shubbak Festival.

The two authors were shortlisted for this year's International Prize for Arabic Fiction for their novels, *Me, She and the Other Women* by Jana Elhassan and *The Beaver* by Mohammad Hasan Alwan, both of which explore the complications of family relations as well as themes of memory and migration. They were presented by UK journalist Bidisha.

The event was hosted by Asia House, and produced by the International Prize for Arabic Fiction.

Photo: Shubbak

CONTRIBUTORS

AUTHORS FROM KUWAIT

Mersel Faleh Al Ajami was born in Kuwait in 1952. He has a BA in Arabic from Kuwait University (1980) and an MA and PhD from the University of Michigan, Ann Arbor (1985 and 1990). He is now Professor of Literature in the department of Arabic Language and Literature at Kuwait University. He has published many studies of critical theory, modern Kuwaiti literature and classical Arabic literature.

Fatima Yousif al-Ali was born in Kuwait in 1953. She is a journalist and short story writer and has a BA in Arabic Literature from Cairo University and an MA in Literary Criticism. She was the first Kuwaiti woman to write a novel (published 1971), and has published four collections of short stories. She won the 1996 Kuwait State Encouragement Award for the Short Story.

Taleb Alrefai was born in Kuwait in 1958. In 1982 he gained his degree in Civil Engineering from the University of Kuwait. He published his first collection of short stories in 1992 and since then has published six more collections and four novels. In 2002, he won the State Prize for Letters for his novel *Ra'ihat al-Bahri* (The Scent of the Sea). He was Chair of Judges of the 2009/2010 International Prize for Arabic Fiction.

Thuraya Al-Baqsami is a Kuwaiti artist and writer, born in Kuwait in 1951. She has a BA and MA from Surikov Arts Institute, Moscow (1974–1981), and has worked as a journalist and illustrator for various Kuwaiti magazines and newspapers since the 1970s. She also writes short stories, children's books and art criticism and has received many awards for her literary and artistic works.

Basima al-Enezi is a Kuwaiti author who published her first short story collection in 1998 under the title *Al-Ashya'* (Things). Her second collection, *Hayatun Khaliyyatun Min al-Ahdath* (An Uneventful Life) won the 2007 Kuwait State Encouragement Award for the Short Story. Her first novel, *Hidha' Aswad 'Ala al-Raseef* (Black Shoes on a Sidewalk), published in 2012 and excerpted in this issue of Banipal, came third in the 2013 Sharjah Prize for Arab Culture.

Bothayna al-Essa is a Kuwaiti author, born in 1982. She has a degree in Business Administration from the University of Kuwait (2005) and an MA in Management, specialising in Finance (2007). She has published five novels and one collection of essays. Her first novel *Irtitam la yusma' lahu dawii* (A Soundless Collision), excerpted above, was published in 2004. She has won many literary awards.

Ali Hussain al-Felkawi is a Kuwaiti author and poet. He has a Masters in History from the Saint Joseph University of Beirut and has published four collections of poetry, the first in 1987. In 2012, his debut novel *Ghuyoum tahta Watrin* (Clouds beneath a Bow String) was published.

Hameady Hamood is an author and story-teller, born in Kuwait in 1973. He has a degree in Mechanical Engineering from Brunel University, UK (2005) and then taught in the College of Technological Studies. He has published many articles in the cultural pages of Kuwaiti newspapers and he has two short story collections, published in 2007 and 2010. He coordinates the programme, Cultural Salon, for Kuwaiti television.

Ismail Fahd Ismail is a Kuwaiti writer, born in Basra, Iraq, in 1940. He spent his childhood in Basra before completing his education in Kuwait, obtaining a BA in Literature and Literary Criticism. Ismail Fahd is considered the spiritual father of the Kuwaiti novel and, from 1965 to 2013, has published 23 novels, two short story collections, three plays and several works of criticism. In 1989, he received the Kuwait State Encouragement Award for the Novel and in 2002, for Literary Criticism.

Suleiman al-Khalifi was born in Kuwait in 1946. He obtained a BA degree in literary criticism from the Higher Institute of Dramatic Arts in Kuwait. He has published a number of poems, stories and critical studies in *Al-Bayan* magazine of the Kuwaiti Writers Association. In 1972 he published a play, *Summer Troubles,* and after that three collections of short stories and a collection of poetry. He has also published two novels, *Aziza* (2008) and *Biban* (2011).

Yousef Khalifa was born in Kuwait in 1977. He is an author, photographer and weekly columnist for the newspaper *Al-Kuwaitiyya.* His published works include a collection of short stories *Al-'Ain al-Thalithah* (The Third Eye), in 2003, and a collection of very short stories *Afkar 'Aariyah* in 2007 (Nude Thoughts, excerpted above in this issue of Banipal). He won the 2008 Laila al-Othman Award for Short Stories and Novels by young writers.

Laila al-Othman was born in Kuwait in 1943. She has written 14 collections of short stories and nine novels. Her best-known novel is *Wasmiya Takhruju min al-Bahr* (Wasmiyya comes out of the Sea), published in 1986, which has been translated into Italian and Russian and was chosen as one of the best 100 Arab novels of the 20th century. In 2004, Al-Othman established the Laila Al-Othman Award for Short Stories and Novels, a biennial prize awarded to young Kuwaiti fiction writers.

Waleed al-Rajeeb was born in Kuwait in 1954. He obtained his BA in Social Service from Helwan University, Egypt, and his Masters in Education from Western Michigan University. From 1983 to 2013 he published 5 short story collections and 5 novels, the first of which, *Badriyya*, was published in 1989, and several works on hypnosis and Reiki. His stories have been translated into English and Polish. Al-Rajeeb received the Kuwait State Award for Letters in 1997 for his short story collection *Qumbar*.

Fawziya Shuwaish al-Salem is a Kuwaiti poet and writer. She has published three novels and three short story collections and two plays. Her latest novel *Salalum al-Nahar* (The Ladder of Day), published in Cairo, in 2012, is excerpted above.

Saud al-Sanousi is a Kuwaiti novelist, journalist and winner of the 2013 International Prize for Arabic Fiction. He was born in 1981. His first novel, *Sijeen al-Maraya* (Prisoner of Mirrors) in 2010, won the Laila al-Othman Award for Short Stories and Novels by young writers. His second novel *Saq al-Bamboo* (The Bamboo Stalk) won the Kuwait State Prize for Letters in 2012 and the 2013 IPAF.

Mona al-Shammari is a Kuwaiti author and journalist. She studied Drama and Theatre at the Higher Institute for Dramatic Arts and has been writing short stories since the late 1980s. Her story *Muwa' al-Jinaza* (The Funeral's Miaow) was awarded the Short Story Prize by the Emirati Writers' Union in 1990. Her first collection of short stories *Yasqut al-Matar, Tamut al-Ameera* (The Rain Falls, the Princess Dies) was published in 2012 (excerpted above).

Hooda Shawa lives in Kuwait and is Kuwaiti by marriage. Born into a Palestinian-British family, she has a degree in Economics and Political Science from the American University in Cairo. Hooda has published three Arabic collections of stories inspired by fables from the Arab and Islamic world. Her book, *The Birds' Journey to Mount Qaf*, based on a Sufi poem, won the Sheikh Zayed Book Award for Children's Literature in 2008.

OTHER CONTRIBUTORS

Charis Bredin has a BA, first class Hons, in French and Arabic from the University of Oxford, and an MA (Distinction) in Arabic Literature from SOAS. She works part-time at Banipal and is starting a PhD at SOAS later this year. She has translated a number of fiction excerpts for Banipal issues.

Andrew C Long received his BA in English and Comparative Literature from Columbia University and his PhD in Comparative Literature from the City University of New York. He currently teaches at Claremont Graduate University. His *Reading Arabia: British Orientalism in the Age of Mass Publication, 1880-1930* (Syracuse University Press) is scheduled for release in November, 2013.

Layla al-Maleh is associate professor of English literature at Kuwait University. She has extensive experience teaching translation courses at both undergraduate and postgraduate levels and worked for many years as a simultaneous interpreter for several international organizations. She is co-translator of *Narrating Kuwait* and is currently preparing to submit a translation into Arabic of literary works by Anglophone Arab writers.

Maxwell Martin is an Arabic enthusiast from New Jersey who currently resides in Washington D.C. He previously worked at the *Daily News Egypt*, an Egyptian newspaper based in Cairo.

Agnes Reeve has a BA Hons in Spanish and Arabic from the University of St Andrews, and is completing an MA in Near and Middle Eastern Studies at SOAS. She currently works part-time at Banipal. She has also studied Arabic at the University of Damascus.

Adam Youssouf is a Chadian writer and journalist living in Kuwait. He has a BA and an MA in Literature and Literary Criticism from the University of Kuwait and has published his poetry and articles in Kuwaiti magazines and newspapers and Arab media. He is editor of the cultural section of the Kuwaiti daily, *Al-Jarida*. He has published one work, *Qasidat al-tafasil al-yawmiyya fi al-shi'r al-khaliji al-mu'asar* (Everyday Details in Contemporary Gulf Poetry).

The translators in Banipal 47 are:

Ruth Ahmedzai, Thomas Aplin, Charis Bredin, Sally Gomaa, Ghenwa Hayek, William M. Hutchins, Layla al-Maleh, Maxwell Martin, Robin Moger, John Peate, Agnes Reeve, Sophia Vasalou, Mona Zaki

The writers and book reviewers are:

Mersel al-Ajami, Taleb Alrefai, Charis Bredin, Andrew C Long, Margaret Obank, Agnes Reeve, Susannah Tarbush, Stephen Watts, Adam Youssouf, Mona Zaki

For information on all the translators, writers and book reviewers in **Banipal 47** and for more on all other contributors, please go to:

www.banipal.co.uk/contributors/